The Silent Teacher
The gift of body donation

CW00819999

Dr. Claire France Smith

Published by Anatomically Correct

First published by Anatomically Correct 2018. Chestnuts, Storrington, RH20 3ET

ISBN 978-1-9995812-0-6

Text © Dr. C Smith.

Front Cover © Miss. H Smith.

Figure 0, 2, 10, 15 © Mr. J Lewis, Clinical Media Centre, Brighton and Sussex University Hospital NHS Trust. Figure 2 SOMSO® Models from Adam, Rouilly.

Figure 18 © Dr. C Smith, with kind permission to print from the Centre for Learning Anatomical Sciences, University of Southampton.

Figure 19 © Anatomy Department, Brighton and Sussex Medical School.

Figure 20 © Dr. R Gonzales, PhD student, Brighton and Sussex Medical School.

Figure 23 © Mr. M Drew, Dignity Funerals.

Figure 36 © Miss. S Chester-Nash, on behalf of the Anatomical Society.

Remaining Figures © Dr. C Smith.

A catalogue record of this book is available from the British Library.

The publisher has made every effort to contact copyright holders of images in this book. Any errors are inadvertent and anyone who for any reason has not been contacted is invited to write to the publisher so that full acknowledgement can be made in subsequent editions of this work.

Published by Anatomically Correct.

Dedication

To my father Michael John Bugler 1949-2016

About the author

I am Head of Anatomy at Brighton and Sussex Medical School in the United Kingdom.

In addition to over 20 years of teaching anatomy and being in an anatomy laboratory, I also have had a wide range of roles that will read a little like I am applying for a job! I want you to understand these and how they contribute to the overall picture that I have explained in this book.

I have been a member of the Court of Examiners for the Royal College of Surgeons for many years, a role that involves examining doctors who wish to be surgeons on their anatomy knowledge. I was elected to the Council of the Anatomical Society and held the role as Chair of the Education Committee, where I guided anatomical educational research strategy and led the development of the anatomy core syllabus that is in place for students training to be doctors in the United Kingdom. I am Secretary General of the European Federation of Experimental Morphologists (Morphology is another word for structure/anatomy), a role that involves promoting and supporting anatomical research within Europe. I am a member of the International Federation of Anatomists Education Committee that guides anatomy education at a global level. On a more local UK level, I am currently Chair of the London and South East Committee of Anatomists. I am also Chair of the Anatomy Associations Advisory Committee that feeds into the Human Tissue Authority and a member of the Human Tissue Authority Stakeholder and Fees group. I think that is enough!

Aside from this, what I really am is a working mum who enjoys nothing more than being at home with my family.

Dr. Claire France Smith

Preface

As a surgeon, anatomical dissection was a life changing experience that had a huge influence on my subsequent career choices. The dissecting room at the University of Sheffield where I trained was an architecturally unique space where the whole year cohort came together on a frequent basis with an additional social dimension that enhanced the learning experience. Five years later I was an anatomy demonstrator at the University of Birmingham, teaching students and preparing prosections myself. These experiences provided the solid foundations every surgeon needs in order to develop their skills and practice safely. Many aspects of this book bring back those anatomical experiences of more than thirty five years ago but also highlight how many things have advanced and improved.

This book is unique in its insight and perspectives into a decision that is well known but little understood. Almost everybody will be aware of the concept of 'leaving one's body to science' but there the understanding ends. The reality is that this represents donating one's body to help with the education of future generations of doctors, dentists, other healthcare professionals and scientists. The body is embalmed and utilised for dissection and the preparation of prosections that may be typically utilised for one or two years and potentially in the case of meticulously prepared prosection specimens, several decades. Making a decision to donate for this purpose is a significant and generous act and until Dr. Smith's book, one that will have been very difficult to research and understand the details and subsequent events.

This book is remarkable in presenting a personal and expert perspective that is inclusive of all the relevant stakeholders including the individual donor, their families and friends, those involved in the care and preparation of their body as well as those who benefit from the learning experience and provide the teaching and support. This process is described in great detail and illustrated with numerous observations and anecdotes. Importantly, Dr. Smith's own experiences and feelings are explored and these will be shared by many who read this book. Dr. Smith is to be congratulated for tackling this sensitive subject and for producing an eminently enjoyable read!

Professor Malcolm Reed, Dean, Brighton and Sussex Medical School

The Silent Teacher

Contents

A letter to the Reader

Dear Reader,

I will take you on a journey through the generous gift of thousands of individuals who donate their body to science. Or, more exactly, to anatomical examination.

I need to include here an explicit warning that some of the text is very descriptive. For some, I understand this will be upsetting. There are pictures of the laboratory space, but all bodies are completely covered up.

I will explain precisely what happens to a donor's body after death and during their time with us. I will also explain what happens when the medical school has concluded work on the donated body.

It might be upsetting when I explain how animal material may be used in medical education. I need to stress that animal material would have been only obtained from the food or pet food production system.

The description of anatomy and of my experiences in different countries is also a difficult subject. I say a little bit about myself and my journey into anatomy at the end of the book.

If you have ever considered body donation, I hope this book answers some of your questions.

If you have had a loved one or friend who has donated their body, I hope you find out how valuable their gift has been to many.

If you are a student considering a career in any subject that involves anatomy, I hope you find this little book informative and encouraging.

If you are none of these, but are reading out of curiosity, I hope you will find it educational and maybe even enlightening.

This book is dedicated to all of those who have donated their bodies to anatomical examination - those that become the Silent Teachers.

Dr. Claire France Smith

Glossary

Accident and Emergency (A&E) – hospital ward for emergencies.

Aneurism- a weak spot in a blood vessel, that causes it to bulge or even burst.

Aorta- main artery leaving the heart, taking blood to the body.

Bequeathal Officer- a person whose role it is to liaise with potential donors, the next of kin when a donor dies and the funeral services.

Brighton and Sussex Medical School (BSMS) – a joint venture between the University of Sussex and the University of Brighton, founded 2004.

Cadaver- a donors dead body

Creutzfeldt-Jakob disease (CJD)- a degenerative brain disorder

Chronic Obstructive Pulmonary Disease (COPD)- progressive lung diseases including emphysema and bronchitis.

Cerebral Spinal Fluid (CSF)- a fluid that circulates around the brain and spinal cord.

Computerised Tomography (CT)- a scan that uses many computer processed x-rays to produce an image of inside the body.

Dissection- to cut apart.

Dissecting Room (DR)- the place where anatomical examination occurs.

Emaciation- unusually thin.

Embalming- a process of preservation.

Fresh Frozen- frozen human bodies/parts that are defrosted prior to use.

General Medical Council (GMC)- the body that regulates the medical profession.

Health Care Assistant (HCA)- a care provider, assisting nurses.

Human Immunodeficiency Virus (HIV)- the virus that damages cells in the immune system, that can cause AIDS.

Human Tissue Authority (HTA)- the body that regulates human tissue and organs under the Human Tissue Act 2004.

Mastication- process of chewing.

Magnetic Resonance Imaging (MRI)- a scan that uses magnetic fields to produce an image of inside the body.

Natural variation- the variation between individuals that is not a result of disease.

Oedema- build-up of fluid in the body that results in an area becoming swollen.

Palpate- examine by touch.

Pneumonia- inflammation of the lungs.

Prosection- a professionally produced dissection.

Standard Operating Procedure (SOP)- step by step instructions for an activity that complies with regulations.

Tuberculosis (TB)- infectious disease caused by bacteria.

Viral hepatitis- is an infection caused by a virus that affects the liver.

Chapter 1. Introduction

Body Donation in the United Kingdom

In the United Kingdom in 2017, around 1,300 donated bodies were accepted by medical schools for anatomy teaching and research. The number of bodies donated has continued to rise over time.

This type of donation is separate from organ donation. The process of body donation is through *'first person consent'* that means that in sound state of mind and over the age of 18, a person can donate their body to science, or the more technical term *'anatomical examination'*. I will explore a lot more about this process in a later chapter (Chapter 2).

The abridged version is that usually within five days of death the donor is collected and then processed (embalmed or frozen) to stop decomposition. Then the body can be used by a range of individuals to learn about the structure and function of a human being. The individuals studying the body include: doctors, medical students, physiotherapists and other healthcare professionals.

An interesting phrase I quite often hear is *'donation to science'*. I have heard there is some confusion about this term from members of the public because donation to science is such a broad term. Individuals can donate organs and tissues to research, or you can donate your body for anatomical examination that will further knowledge and the treatment of health and disease. Both are covered under the wider term donation to science.

At the time of death the deceased person, once accepted, becomes known as a *'donor'*. The donor is referred to only by their identity details for example, Mr A. Smith Date Of Birth 01/01/1948 Date Of Death 01/01/2018. After the donor has been collected they are taken to a medical school to be embalmed. The donor becomes known as a *'cadaver'* and is assigned a number for example, 385. The cadaver will be held and used by the medical school for up to three years. At the end of this time they are returned to a coffin and are assigned their name back and then become known as a donor again. There is much more information on this later.

As you would expect the whole process is tightly regulated and the Human Tissue Authority (HTA) was established as the governing body to regulate the removal, storage, use and disposal of human bodies, organs and tissue in accordance with the Human Tissue Act of 2004, that covers England, Northern Ireland and Wales. There are separate Acts for Scotland (Human Tissue Act Scotland 2006) and Ireland (Anatomy Act 1832), although the principles are very much aligned. The term Human Tissue is defined as material that has come from a human body and consists of, or includes, human cells. The Human Tissue Authority regulates the Act through a series of codes of practice. The first code covers consent and is applicable to all sectors. The different sectors include; organ transplantation, research, post mortem examination, and anatomical examination, amongst others. Anatomical examination is the focus of this book.

Research

The research sector covers the donation of both living and dead tissue. This will be a specific organ, tissue or cell type. For example, while taking a biopsy a research project with consent will take a sample of that biopsy so that it can be further studied in a laboratory by scientists tackling a certain disease, such as cancer. The research sector also covers the donation of specific parts of the body for research. A good example are brain banks. Brain banks take donations of brain and spinal cord tissue to allow researchers to understand better about conditions, such as dementia. Brain banks might be more known to individuals who are suffering with a condition and have thought about this donation specifically. Donating your brain and spinal cord does not stop you from donating other organs.

Organ Donation and Transplantation

The organ donation and transplantation sector regulates the donation of organs and tissue (groups of cells) from living and deceased individuals into other living individuals. This includes the removal of organs such as the kidney, heart, skin or eyes et cetera, from a deceased individual that is transplanted into the living. The sector also covers tissue not needed by a living donor such as bone that is removed during hip replacement surgery and is donated into a bank to be used by another patient. Organ transplantation also involves the removal of an organ from a living person for example, part of a liver or a kidney that is then transplanted into a living recipient. If you have signed an organ donor card, or not opted out of a system that operates on deemed consent, then your body can be used for organ donation but will not be used for anatomical examination.

Post-Mortem

The post-mortem sector involves the regulation of what happens to your body if the cause of death needs to be established. This involves the examination of the body (autopsy) by a Pathologist to make recommendations about the cause of death. A post-mortem will be requested by a coroner in circumstances where an individual has died un-expectedly because of or, following a sudden or violent incident. During the post-mortem, it could be necessary to retain samples of tissue as evidence. The main aim here would be to decide if an inquest was required. An inquest is the legal investigation into the circumstances of death. A hospital doctor can also request a post-mortem to find out about the medical cause of death, and to further research and medical understanding. This can only occur with consent given by the individual before they died or from the next of kin. Typically, post-mortems are carried out two to three days after death. The pathologist will cut into the body and depending on the need for the post-mortem will focus on certain areas. The post-mortem can involve the removal of organs or tissue for further analysis. After the pathologist has completed their report the body will be released to the family for funeral arrangements to be made.

Anatomical Examination
The anatomical examination (anatomy) sector is about the donation of a body to a medical school for the development of knowledge. This involves teaching, development of surgical and clinical practice and research related to anatomy. Anatomical Examination is the focus of this book.

What is Anatomy?

Anatomy refers to the structural organisation of a living organism. In Greek it translates to mean dissect. Anatomy includes many sub-disciplines - gross anatomy, surface anatomy, histology, neuroanatomy and embryology.

Gross Anatomy
Gross Anatomy (also known as topographical anatomy) is the study of the human body that can be seen with the human eye. Gross anatomy includes bones, muscles, organs, nerves, arteries and veins. Historically the study of gross anatomy has been through dissection of donated bodies. Understanding of gross anatomy is essential for many professions including doctors, physiotherapists, nurses, et cetera. Gross anatomy also includes natural variation. We are all unique and while our body is in many ways the same as everyone else's, we may have some

specific known differences. Some individuals have extra or missing muscles, some have a different pattern of arteries and veins. Doctors need to know about common variations to safely treat patients.

Surface Anatomy
Surface anatomy (also known as superficial anatomy) is the examination of the external features (surface) of the body. Surface anatomy includes the projection of structures beneath the skin onto the surface, for example where a stethoscope would be placed on the chest to listen to the heart valves. Surface anatomy also includes the location of structures that can be felt (palpated) through the skin, for example the bony prominences of the styloid processes on your wrist (the sticky out bit). Surface Anatomy is essential in clinical practice, for example doctors need to know what anatomical structures are underneath the skin and where the nerve networks go to make the pain be felt by the patient. Pain networks are complex and even though pain may be felt near the belly button this might not be where the actual pain is coming come.

Histology
Histology (also known as microscopic anatomy) is the study of anatomical structures but at a micro level, and to study histology a microscope is needed. At a histological level, it is possible to identify different types of tissue (certain types of cells grouped together, for example, muscle tissue), individual cells and their interconnections. Understanding histology is important for understanding disease. Scientists often work at a histological level to study cells in health and disease. Doctors must understand the body at a histological level to be able, for example, to understand different types of tumours and how they might affect surrounding structures. The word Histo is derived from Greek and means 'tissues'.

Neuroanatomy
Neuroanatomy is the study of structures of the nervous system. This includes the brain and spinal cord. Neuroanatomy is closely integrated with understanding the function of the brain, with different professions studying neuroanatomy to understand its inner workings. These include doctors, dentists, nurses, psychologists and scientists.

Embryology
Embryology is the sub-discipline that deals with how the human body forms. Embryology covers the time from conception until birth when the specialities of neonatology (care of newborn) and then paediatrics (care of children) take over. Understanding embryology is important for knowing how malformations occur and their treatment.

Pathology

Pathology seeks to understand what has happened in disease. Pathology simply means the path from which disease comes. Doctors need to understand what has happened to the body in disease in order to make a diagnosis and to advise on the more appropriate treatment.

Radiology

Radiology uses medical imaging to assist with a diagnosis and is also involved in the treatment of many conditions. Radiology uses various imaging techniques such as x-ray, Computed Tomography (CT), Magnetic Resonance Imaging (MRI) and ultrasound. Anatomist are experts in the structure of the human body but at the same time, while not an expert, they cover areas of pathology and radiology because they are so closely related.

When educating doctors and allied health professionals all these sub disciplines need to come together to create a whole picture. As an example, to understand the functions of the brain students must study the brain itself. They also need to understand the arterial supply of the brain. This is gross anatomy. There also needs to be an understanding of embryology and how the brain has come to be in its final shape based on its growing from a tube and folding on itself. It is important to know how these arteries branch and divide and what occurs in a stroke. This is pathology. Anatomists also teach about the functional consequences of an interrupted blood supply and how this could present when the doctor is assessing the patient. For example, in a stroke the surface anatomy features are a drooping mouth and paralysis. Students must also understand how the changes in the brain caused by a stroke would be viewed clinically on an MRI scan. This is radiology. The understanding of histology of the arteries and the way that the brain receives oxygen is of importance for the mechanism of drug treatment.

Now I am not claiming that anatomists are experts at all of these things. Anatomists teach on all of the areas mentioned above and are joined by experts in these areas during teaching sessions. This creates a learning environment where students are learning what they need to for clinical practice in an applied way. Hopefully, long gone are the days when students learn facts for the sake of it. Historically it was believed that every doctor should know everything there was to know. With the volume of information expanding the focus has shifted much more to doctors only knowing the information they need to know. Information is so accessible in society, as a result fine detail has moved into specialist training as and when this is needed. This shift means that today's medical education is far more applied to knowing the information, being able to reconstruct and interpret the knowledge in different settings and applying the knowledge as needed.

Who are Anatomists?

An Anatomist is simply an expert in anatomy. I have found that an internet search of how to become an anatomist is amusing; such phrases as 'strong in academics' and 'emotionally stable' occur! Other characteristics include; curiosity, intellect and patience. I am not sure whether I should be laughing at these or agreeing! Anatomists work within universities and are individuals with a high level of academic qualifications that include first degrees, masters and PhDs. Anatomists either predominately work in areas of research, or they work solely in the teaching field. Anatomists often have their own research profile in an area for example, neuroanatomy but also teach gross anatomy.

As an Anatomist, I feel that I have an amazing and varied career. There are a few characteristics that I do feel anatomists must have. Firstly, knowledge, passion and an understanding of the human body. Secondly, a strong stomach. Thirdly, good problem solving skills. Finally, a dark sense of humour to keep us sane!

There is a hierarchical structure that exists in the roles in academic life. Research individuals will start off at the junior post of Lecturer, then progress to Senior Lecturer, then Reader and the highest post, Professor. Anatomists who predominantly teach rather than carry out research are often titled a Teaching Fellow, Senior Teaching Fellow, Principle Teaching Fellow or Professorial Teaching Fellow. In the United States for example these strands are the same as Assistant Professor, Associate Professor and Professor, irrespective of the balance of teaching and research.

Within anatomy there are professional services or technical posts. There is a post unique to anatomy, the Prosector. The Prosector is a person whose role it is to prepare, cut up and make expert dissections, a kind of *'here's one I prepared earlier'* (known at prosections). The Prosector often also manages the laboratory environment, *'the Dissecting Room'.* The number of prosector posts that I am aware of in the United Kingdom is of the order of 20. A couple of years ago I needed to advertise for this post. The University provides a generic job description for all posts based on their grade. For the prosector post this took a lot of rewriting to make it suitable for the job role of a Prosector. I then had a laugh to myself when Human Resources said that this job will be advertised for internal re-deployment unless I could provide a case as to why not. My email back stated that unless they can expertly cut up and work with dead bodies I was not prepared to consider a re-deployment!

Prosectors are often supported by anatomy technicians of different grades. Anatomy technicians assist with the care of the donated bodies and are responsible for many day-to-day tasks such as helping set up for teaching sessions.

Often a group of individuals called Anatomy Demonstrators work within an anatomy team. Anatomy demonstrators frequently work as teachers helping in dissecting room sessions. They also take small groups of students for tutorials on a specific area of anatomy such as neuroanatomy.

The anatomy demonstrator role varies between institutions. The post can be a fixed term contract (9 or 12 months) where a junior doctor (two or three years after qualifying) takes a year out to work in an anatomy department teaching and working on a research project. Sometimes these posts are funded by a private health care provider and the doctors work shifts for the private hospital and then work at the university for the rest of the time. Some posts are part of a wider training programme. All doctors who are registered on the early part of surgical training (formally known as Core Surgical Training) are required to undertake thirty anatomy sessions over the course of twelve months. At other institutions, the post may be paid for by the university and the individual does not need to have a medical qualification but can have just a degree in science. Many PhD students during the first or second year of their course in a related discipline, for example, neuroanatomy or embryology, are often required to undertake several sessions where they act as an anatomy demonstrator. This helps build their experience and their CV. Some anatomy demonstrators are retired or semi-retired clinicians who return to the anatomy laboratory to share their wealth of experience with younger demonstrators and students. A core part of having anatomy demonstrators for me is that they inject very current medical practice into the DR, that enables students to link learning to practice.

A typical day as an Anatomist

The following description of my typical day will hopefully give you an idea of what will follow later in the book. My day starts early, as with any working mum. Getting children up, fed, dressed and out the door for school is a major daily achievement. I start teaching at 9am, so I need to be at work around 8 a.m. to check everything is set up and to get the rest of the teaching team ready. I am dressed in a black work suit, ready for my afternoon lecture. It has been commented about how often I wear black, feeling it is related to death but this is not the intention. Black is easy to buy, easy to wear, and it lasts - simple. I swipe the sensor on my wrist and go into the teaching laboratory, otherwise known as the Dissecting Room or DR. I go through the student changing room and into the staff office, say good morning to the team and go straight into the staff changing room to put on my scrubs. There are different colours of scrubs for different roles within the laboratory. Faculty staff - black, junior doctors- blue and technical staff- wine, don't ask why wine colour, they chose it! There are allocated DR shoes - mine are white and are a famous flip flop brand that are like clogs, although they don't stay white for long.

I go into the main teaching space and check the projector and technology works to show a short presentation. I also put on my microphone headset (imagine Britney Spears in concert!) and say a few *'testing, one, two, three, testing'*. I check that each one of the nine cadavers to be studied are prepared and are suitable for the session. If anything is not I can quickly ask the team to assist. I am looking to check that each donor is lying on its back, that the initial saw marks made by the team are correct, that each table has the right instruments (saw, chisel, various forceps, scalpels et cetera.) and that each table has an iPad, printed instructions and some plastic skulls.

Today's session is a year two medical student dissection session. Currently there are 140 medical students on each year of the course. The year is split into two groups of 70 for their anatomy sessions and the students work in groups of eight around a donor. At times there may be one or two students dissecting, one or two students may be assisting. The other students will be using resources such as the iPad, models and skeletons to learn about the body. The students then swap around so each student has an opportunity to dissect, assist and learn through another resource.

The aim of today's session is to remove the brain and to examine the surrounding structure (dural sinuses) and the nerves that leave the brain (cranial nerves). Students will also look at the blood supply to the brain and the surface of the brain. This session is going to take from 9-11a.m.

I then go back into the DR office to see the anatomy demonstrators who have arrived to teach. Some have taught here before, others not. So, I give a quick induction and a review of the anatomy to be covered. For any students reading this, it might appear to be last minute actions, but the demonstrators are junior doctors who have spent two years working in the United Kingdom National Health Service (NHS). They have learnt this material recently and are used to being responsive and adaptive. It is then time for a very quick cup of tea. At 8.50 a.m. the year two medical students start to arrive. The students need to put on surgical gowns, gloves and eye protection before they enter the DR.

Each teaching session starts with a presentation on the large screen in the DR. This short presentation goes through the description of the tasks for the session. The students are then shown an example of the work they should complete. This is undertaken by an operating theatre light with a built-in camera.

A few days earlier I had removed the skull from a cadaver and removed the brain for the anatomy demonstrators to see. This had taken an hour and it was fascinating to see all the structures that surround the brain. Even though I have undertaken this many times before, I am always amazed at how well protected our brain is by bone and connective tissue (dura mater). A lot of medicine is a *'watch one, do one, teach one'* model and anatomy is very much like that too.

The students are in awe of seeing a real brain being removed. As am I to be honest. The students would have seen a real human brain in their first year but this session will be the first time they have ever held one. I can tell there is an air of excitement and in trepidation. As a teacher, I can also see that the students are concentrating hard, taking in the amount of work they are going to have to do over the next two hours. I let the students get on with it and the next two hours pass in a flash of sawing, having my hands inside a skull, explaining concepts and repeatedly saying *'keep one hand on that brain otherwise you will tear the nerves'!* I cannot share pictures of this with you, but Figure 2 was taken during the session when Catherine and myself were at the front of the class using models to explain a concept. Some students have listened to instructions. Around an hour later they can free the brain and remove it from the cavity. They hold the brain proudly like a new baby. Others, for various reasons, have hit some trouble and the brain has come out in two, three or four pieces. The students examine the brain and the now empty cavity in the skull. The brain is a beautiful structure, its curves and grooves (gyri and sulci) create a pattern on its surface. On the base of the brain you can find the nerves that are passing information away to the face and other regions (cranial nerves). A fact that I find amazing, is the brain is floating in fluid (cerebral spinal fluid, CSF), if it didn't float it would crush the vital nerves that leave the brain.

When the end of the session arrives, the students wash up and clean down - more on this later (Chapter 3). I am now slightly messy. I have leaned on a wet cloth on a table and I have a wet line across my stomach. I give my hands and arms a good wash and get changed out of my scrubs (that go for washing). I then have a conversation with the laboratory team about a donor who died over the weekend. There is information coming in about the donor and on reviewing the cause of death and known health conditions it is decided to accept the donation. There is then a thirty minute catch up with the Prosector about an external audit of the DR facility that is being planned.

Next I return to my office ready to meet Catherine, one of my PhD students. Catherine is undertaking a PhD on the use of social media in medical education and works in the department as a Teaching Fellow. Her PhD is so current, and is showing what students feel about social media and how this changes as they become professionals. Each of my PhD students has a monthly meeting to go through the work that they have been doing, planning or writing. Next I eat a sandwich. At 1 p.m. there is a meeting about an event that we are running for the British Science Festival. This meeting is about logistics and how the inner workings of the human body can be shown to the public. After the meeting there is 10 minutes to refocus my attention on the previously prepared lecture notes. In this case, I have given this lecture for the last four years, so it's just a brief refresher. Another quick cup of tea goes down and head to the lecture theatre.

This lecture called the 'Introduction to the Human Body' is for first year medical students. They sit making notes, tapping on their laptop keys with each word I say. I can tell that the students have had enough of introduction lectures and are quite relieved when the context moves on to how the body forms as an embryo. I enjoy giving lectures but also find them draining, you put all your energy and enthusiasm into an hour's performance. I feel that the lecture went well and at the end of my talk many of the students approach me to ask about various things. Some just want to confirm a point, others are a little worried about going into the DR. I ensure that I spend the time with students because it is important to their learning experience. It also reminds me of being a student myself and how helpful some lecturers were and the difference it made. Next, I return to my office in need of a snack (chocolate). It is now 3:30 p.m. and I meet with my PA (Lisa) who has a quick list of things to download. Next I look at the long list of emails that have collected. I approve some finance items and answer a few student questions before looking at the lecture that I am giving tomorrow on Cranial Nerves (the ones that emerge from the base of the brain). It is time to go home, collect my children, cook tea, help with homework, do bath time et cetera. and before finally sitting down around 9 p.m. having a quick look at a teaching topic for some anaesthetists tomorrow afternoon.

You might be thinking, that's a long day, but don't university lecturers get long holidays? Sadly not. A typical day when the students are not present would include a two-hour meeting about some area of curriculum planning, assessment, et cetera. Then I would pop into the DR either to have a look at a new prosection that has been dissected or I might be at a meeting with a clinician who wishes to run a surgical course in the DR. During times when there is a reduction in my teaching schedule I am trying to start, make progress on, finish or revise a journal research paper.

So that is an example of a normal day.

Figure 1. Standard Lecture Theatre but I had asked the students to send in questions via paper airplanes.

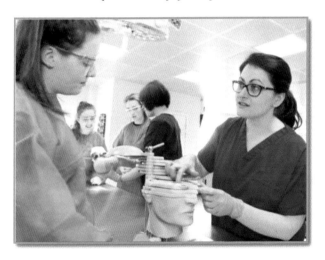

Figure 2. Catherine (right) and myself teaching students using models of the skull and head (*SOMSO® Models from Adam, Rouilly*)

Chapter 2. Donating your body

Donation is the act of giving and, in this case, it is the individuals' wish to give their body. This is also known as a *'bequeathal'*.

Why do individuals donate their body?

I often wonder what makes an individual decide to donate their body. At various memorial services that are either arranged by a medical school or by a group of medical schools, such as the London Anatomy Office, I am privileged to speak to donors' families. Some do say a little more about their loved one's decision to donate.

For one family, their mother had been a biology teacher in a school and had decided many years previously that she wanted to continue to teach in her death, and body donation was a natural choice for her. For another family, they joked how much their father had held strong feelings against religion and that in his words, *'he had used and abused his body in every possible way - what possible use was it for him when there was no afterlife?'* He felt that if someone else could use it and, in his words, abuse it in a different way, it suited him. Please note a body would never be abused - this was his humour and perspective on his own body.

Other families have often told me of a disease that their relative had received treatment for and how they were very grateful to the doctors and healthcare professionals who helped them. They felt that body donation was there way of giving something back to the healthcare professionals' training. One family explained how their mother had died from pancreatic cancer and how it had spread. Over a couple of years, she had undergone many treatments and been under the care of many healthcare teams. She had been examined by junior doctors and had taken an interest in their training. The family commented on how she was impressed by their keenness and yet softer understanding of her concerns as a patient when she spoke to them in person. The family explained that body donation was something their mother said she had heard of many years ago and it was only when it became clear she was not going to beat the cancer that she donated her body. The family were interested in what types of things their mother's body would have been used for and so I explained a little. The family seemed pleased that other junior doctors in training would have been able to see her cancer and learn from it.

One family told be about the pioneering surgery their brother had undergone following a motorbike accident many years previously that had affected his jaw. He had undergone several operations that eventually made his jaw function as normal. He had made the decision to donate his body after the surgeons had explained how they had practiced the operation on donors. His family said he wanted to do the same and he also registered as an organ donor. Some 60 years later his health had deteriorated from old age and when he died his sister confirmed with a doctor that he would not be suitable for organ donation. This made the next decision easy, his sister knew he had donated his body for anatomy, and in her words, all she had to do was to phone the medical school, as *'he was on the books'.*

The options surrounding what to do after death have traditionally been aligned to specific religious beliefs. A study in 1995 asked potential donors why they chose to donate. The study had 218 responses, of these 98 individuals (45%) said they were not religious. It might be that body donation was and perhaps still is a common option that is aligned to individuals who do not believe in a *'god'* or *'higher being'.* However, for those with specific religious beliefs some have reflected informally to me that the idea of body donation, as a selfless act to help others, is very much in keeping with their own religion. For other religions body donation would be at odds with their belief as to what should occur after death. For example, in Islam and in Judaism, the body should be buried as soon as possible, ideally within 24- 48 hours so that the body does not decompose, that the religion view as being disrespectful. The use of embalming is also perceived as disrespectful. Despite this donations from these religious groups have been accepted, although the number is very few.

I have also heard that a donor donated because they were born before the National Health Service (NHS) came into being in 1948 and felt they had received great service from it over their years and wanted to give back to it. Truly remarkable!

Other future donors have told me that they chose to donate their body after their mother or father did the same. I have found this common, that sometimes when one person has found out about body donation they then explain it to their family and friends who then decide to undertake it too. I have a personal experience of this that I describe later.

Financial considerations could influence the choice made by an individual to donate. With the average cost of a funeral in the United Kingdom being £4,000, the number of *public health* funerals has risen in recent years. These are funerals previously known as *paupers'* or *welfare* funerals. In 2013-14 in the United Kingdom, 2,580 public health funerals were undertaken, where the Local Authority has a duty to undertake the funeral where no other arrangements can or have been made.

When an individual donates their body, the associated costs of transport and cremation are covered by the medical school. For such funerals, it might be that an individual choses to donate because they do not have the funds for a funeral or do not wish family to cover the costs. It might be that they do not wish to have a funeral at all. If cost is an issue the individual may not be aware of public health funerals and it is important that body donation is not seen as means to decrease the amount of public health funerals or that individuals feel pushed into this by cost.

Who can donate their body?

In the UK, you can donate your body if you are over 18 years of age and of sound mind, and there is no upper age limit - the oldest individual so far to donate within London and the South East was 106. To give an idea of volume, within London there are over 17,000 donors on the database, although impossible to know the accuracy of this as an individual will donate and then may move away from the area, or they might die and their family were unaware of their donation wishes and records have not been removed.

Donation in the England and Wales is organised by the proximity of a postcode region to a local medical school. For example, if you live in the postcodes BB, CH, FY, IM, L, LA, PR, WA, WN then your donation will go to the University of Liverpool. This information is available in the back of the book and is on the HTA website (www.hta.gov.uk). If you live in Scotland or Ireland there is a similar system. However, if you live outside of the United Kingdom you cannot donate your body to a United Kingdom medical school.

You might be wondering about how many people donate. Numbers across the United Kingdom have risen over time, but so has demand. In 2001, a study revealed 670 bodies were accepted for donation, in 2005 this had decreased to 600. This might be due to donation registrations reducing or to lower demand for donors that meant more donors were turned down. However, since 2005 donation and demand numbers have steadily increased. In 2017, London alone accepted 320 donors. In the United Kingdom in 2017, 1,300 donated bodies were accepted by all medical schools.

You also might be wondering, whether you can donate your old aunt or if your grandson, who you might have never liked, could donate you against your will. Thankfully, the answer in the United Kingdom is no to both. The technical term for this is *'Second Person Consent'*. Under the previous Anatomy Act of 1984 it was considered acceptable to take the word of the next of kin. Hence, if they said that their relative had indicated that they would like their body to be donated they could donate them. Of course, this did mean that some less scrupulous families did donate family members' bodies on their death, perhaps to avoid the funeral costs.

In the United Kingdom, since the Human Tissue Act 2004 was enacted, all consent must now be *'First Person Consent'*. This does mean that sadly there are individuals out there who have genuinely said to their nearest and dearest *'I want you to donate my body to medicine'*, but when the time comes medical schools are unable to take them because consent can only be formally recognised by an Anatomy Act 1984 form signed by the individual who is donating, or on a Human Tissue Act form again signed by the individual who is donating. Alternatively, a donation can be accepted if it is specified in a will, signed by the individual.

There are different points in time when individuals decide to donate their body. For some it is a clear wish from the age of 18. For others, it is after the death of a parent or grandparent that has brought the issue of their own mortality to the front of their mind. It is for others when suffering from a condition or disease and they think about the training their doctors received, or the medical advances that have helped them. The final group of individuals is the elderly, who are deciding their wishes for after their death.

Death and dying is still a taboo subject and no one really likes to think about it or talk about it. I think it's healthy to think that you started life as two cells joining, you duplicated again, and soon became millions of cells that make up your physical body, that will eventually wear out. You don't (always) have a choice as to when you die. But you do have a choice as to what you would prefer to happen to your body when you die. Your family or your solicitor can only act on this information if you tell them and record that decision in a recognised way.

The need for donors is not well advertised to the public. Advertisement is not against the law but perhaps felt to be unethical. There is a fine line between actively recruiting donors and providing the public with information that clearly states that this is an option after death. It simply may be that this choice is not known to everyone. This is something that I hope will change.

Around 2003, my manager at the time was invited to an end of life forum, to speak about body donation. She was not interested in attending the event and asked if I would like to go instead. I was not sure what to expect but they had asked so I went. It was in a modern church hall and the death and dying event seemed to be busy when I got there. I soon realised that dying was a big business. Everyone else had a stall and had brought posters, booklets, freebies et cetera. I had simply just turned up. Individuals were already walking around looking at the stalls. All I could do was just stand there behind a table. I quickly made a sign saying body donation and placed it on the table in front of me. Maybe this was a lack of planning error but I don't think back then anyone would have done any different! The organiser was aware that I looked out of place so after people had time to mingle (I thought you only mingled at parties!) the organiser asked the guests to sit and invited a few stall holders to just answer a few questions. He kindly introduced me and in a few minutes, I explained what body donation involved. I made it clear that this was not advertising and if they wished to receive any further information to place their name on the list on the table by the door. I never knew if anyone of the individuals I saw that night ended up in a DR.

How to donate your body

The law requires that a donation must be in writing and must be witnessed prior to the person's death. There are specific guidelines if the person cannot write.

There are two possible ways that you can donate your body:

1. Through a consent form.

2. Through a Will.

Through a consent form.

If you are thinking of donating please visit the Human Tissue Authority webpage (www.hta.gov.uk), or use the list in the back of this book to contact your nearest licensed medical school or surgical training centre. The medical school or surgical training centre will take your details and will send you in the post a donation pack. You should take time to read this and if you wish to donate your body, complete the consent form and return it to the medical school.

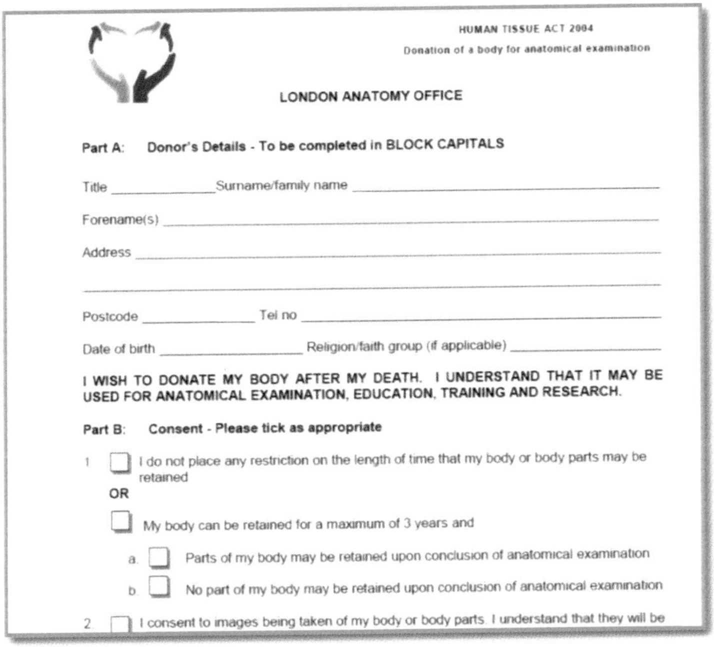

HUMAN TISSUE ACT 2004

Donation of a body for anatomical examination

LONDON ANATOMY OFFICE

Part A: **Donor's Details - To be completed in BLOCK CAPITALS**

Title ____________ Surname/family name ______________________

Forename(s) ______________________

Address ______________________

____

Postcode ____________ Tel no ______________________

Date of birth ____________ Religion/faith group (if applicable) ____________

I WISH TO DONATE MY BODY AFTER MY DEATH. I UNDERSTAND THAT IT MAY BE USED FOR ANATOMICAL EXAMINATION, EDUCATION, TRAINING AND RESEARCH.

Part B: **Consent - Please tick as appropriate**

1 ☐ I do not place any restriction on the length of time that my body or body parts may be retained

OR

☐ My body can be retained for a maximum of 3 years and

a. ☐ Parts of my body may be retained upon conclusion of anatomical examination

b. ☐ No part of my body may be retained upon conclusion of anatomical examination

2. ☐ I consent to images being taken of my body or body parts. I understand that they will be

Figure 3. Sample consent form (not to be used for donation - full forms must be obtained from a medical school)

If you have already signed the old Anatomy Act forms and a medical school has these records, or if you have already signed forms with a medical school since 2004 under the HTA regulations, there is nothing further to do other than to ensure your family and friends are aware of your decision.

Through a Will.

Donation through a Will is still a legal option, although for reasons I will explain, I would recommend anyone considering body donation to use the consent forms described previously rather than this option.

There can be difficulties if the donation is just via a Will. Donation is time sensitive and Wills are often not read for days after someone has died. I took a phone call where a solicitor had found out that an individual wanted to donate their body. This was a good 10 days after the death and they were calling to see how it all worked. Sadly, it was too late by then as the body could not be accepted that long after death.

The other issue with Wills are that they are often very generic and do not detail specific areas of consent. I have seen some that just say *'I wish to donate my body'*. This statement does not state for which use. A statement that says, *'I wish to donate my body to medical teaching'* gives a greater level of consent as to what individual intended their donated body to be used for. Often the lawful term *'Anatomical Examination'* is not mentioned. The current law recognises that Anatomical Examination is not a term the public or solicitors are familiar with. Therefore, a donation can be accepted if there is sufficient evidence that the donation was intended for Anatomical Examination.

I can give you another example to think about. In another Will, the information stated that the individual wished to donate their body for therapeutics, organ transplant and medical research. What do you think this person wanted to happen to their body? This raises questions about what they meant by each term.

- How did they intend their body to be used for therapeutics? Therapeutics is something that has a healing effect. Did they mean drug discovery?
- Taking the term medical research - did they intend their brain or another organ to go to a tissue bank or did they mean body donation for anatomy?
- Was there an intention here for their body to be used for education?

Organ transplant in this example is clear. In some cases where the wording is not as precise as is needed to be, it is possible to go back to the family (if there is a next of kin) and ask them to clarify in writing the intention. This is within the codes of practice issued by the HTA. Personally, I do not feel easy about doing this as donation to anatomy might not have been what they wished – can I confirm First Person Consent in this situation?

I also came across a situation while completing this book where a donor had ticked a box on a care home sheet about what they would like to happen to their body after death. The box simply said cremation, burial, religious service and *'donation to medical science'*. This one tick box for body donation is not enough legal consent and could result on donation being turned away, the donor having assumed this was all they needed to do. I ended up speaking to the care provider (a national company) to help them make changes to this form. The result was it was changed it to a tick box that asked for information on body donation, so that an individual could be helped to request the correct donation forms, rather than the form being seen as a method of consent.

Wills also are not always clear on expectations on retention of body parts, or what they wish to happen to the body after donation. Where is it not explicitly stated I do not infer anything. Hence, I would not permit retention after three years or consent for images if a person in the Will had not specified this.

There is only one reason where consent of the individual before death is not required. This is if 100 years have lapsed since the time of death. This mechanism means that anatomy departments can continue to keep existing historical specimens and take in newly found historical specimens. I will give some examples of the things that people really do find and bring into anatomy departments later in the book (Chapter 6).

If you have concerns about your wishes being properly represented legally in your will, there is no need to incur any costs with a solicitor to check – just contact your local medical school (see the end of the book) and complete the relevant forms in addition.

No matter what way you may choose to register your consent to donate, you must ensure that your next of kin and other family & friends are aware of your donation wishes, as this can really help to ensure your body is accepted given the time constraints - there is currently no system in place to automatically identify that registered donors have died.

What happens when you die

When a donor dies, their relative, next of kin, solicitor or doctor contacts their nearest medical school. In London and the associated postcodes (refer to table at the end of the book for postcodes) it is Kim and Sarah at the London Anatomy Office. This sounds quite grand but the London Anatomy Office is a humble two small rooms rented in Kings College. Kim will ask the relatives some questions about the donor, time, place of death and some medical history. This information usually comes from a doctor or healthcare professional who has cared for the potential donor. It is fine if several members of the family contact the office to inform them of the death of a relative, it is better to have overlap than for each family member to assume that another person has done it. The next of kin only needs to phone once the death has occurred, sometimes there are phone calls of *'we think it will be this weekend'*. I particularly remember one occasion, where a wife phoned the medical school nearly every Friday for several weeks to say, *'it will be soon'*. It was kind of her to let us know and to be thinking about what her husband wanted but it wasn't necessary. I hope that in some way it helped her to process what was happening and what would eventually occur.

The London Anatomy Office do not make the decision as to whether the donor is accepted. They only make the decision whether someone is suitable to be referred to the London and South East Medical schools. The decision of whether a donor can be accepted is made by a named person (s) who is responsible for this at the institution (i.e. me or one of my team who is listed on the HTA licence). Everyone is trained to make this decision and are aware of the many factors that influence it.

Once there is confirmation that the donation can be accepted, the next part depends on local arrangements. If the donor has died at home or in a nursing home they will need to be transferred to a local funeral home where they can be kept in a suitable cold facility. If the donor has died at a hospital or hospice the death can be certified and the body stored. The body will later be collected by the funeral services that work for the medical school. Once suitability has been established, the funeral services then transfer the donor in a private ambulance to the local medical school. On arrival, the donor is checked to confirm they are who all the documentation says, including the details on the card attached to the coffin (known as the coffin card) and identify tags placed on the donor's wrist/ankle. This check is very detailed, as you can imagine we would not want to have the wrong body. Documentation records and traceability of donations is critical to being able to continue to receive and use donations in the United Kingdom and to meet the regulatory requirements of the HTA.

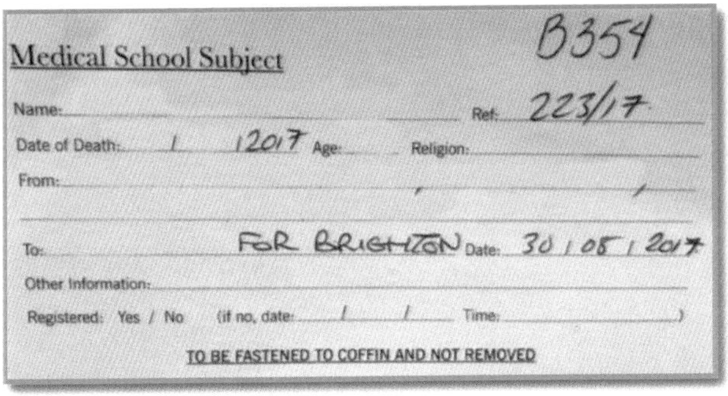

Figure 4. Sample Coffin Card (identity hidden)

Why a donor might not be accepted

Earlier I stated that in 2017, in London 217 donors were not accepted. It is therefore important to communicate that the gift of donation might not be possible. There are numerous reasons why a donation might not be accepted at the time of death. I will explain the common ones, but I cannot cover them all because there are some situations that might make an individual identifiable.

Medical Conditions
There are some medical conditions that a donor might have that make a donation impossible to accept because they could pose a risk of transmission of disease to staff and students. An example of conditions currently not accepted are hepatitis, active TB or HIV because of the risk of infection. It is also not possible to accept a donor if they have had early onset dementia because of the risk of prions (prions are infectious proteins that are found in conditions such as CJD).

There are certain conditions that can make it difficult to embalm a donor. A burst aortic aneurism (the aorta is the major artery carrying blood away from your heart) will make it impossible for the embalming fluid to be pumped around your body. Another example is where recent surgery has occurred and the wound has not healed. This could result in the embalming fluid, that goes through the body to stop decomposition, simply pouring out. Severe bedsores or oedema is problematic in enabling the embalming fluid to move around the body. A severe deformity either as a result of trauma, for example, if the individual has been involved in a road traffic accident, or a deformity linked to a genetic condition, for example a deformity of the spine, may not be accepted as this makes it difficult to keep the body flat on the embalming table.

You may be wondering how research into the conditions mentioned above occurs if donors with such conditions are not accepted. These conditions are not suitable for anatomical examination but this research does occur. An institution with an HTA research licence, with appropriate consent, will undertake research to aid understanding of these conditions. In these examples cells, tissues or organs that have been affected by the condition are used in the research.

Local need
The acceptance of a body also depends on need. In simple terms, if a certain group of surgeons will be using donors to explore the abdomen and are not concerned about the lungs, it will not matter if a donor has had a major respiratory disease as long as the rest of the body is fine. Within the London group if one medical school refuses a donor, the information about the donor will be passed on to another school. The London Anatomy Office manages each medical school's requirements based on what they have requested. It can be that one medical school needs a certain number of donors for a time in the year based on the curriculum. There is also a need to keep a watch on the balance of the sex of donors going to each school. All medical schools teach the reproductive system and hence need donors both female and male. This is carried out by the medical schools.

Logistics
There are logistical timeframes that are in place that might prevent a donation being accepted. There might be a couple of donors being embalmed at that point in time, and therefore it is not possible to take another -this is often the case for medical schools who only have facilities to process one or two donors at a time. It might be that a donor cannot be taken simply due to the institution being full. If it is not possible for a donor to be accepted because of logistical reason, contact is made with equivalent institutions nearby to see if they can take the donation instead.

If the donor has a post mortem then this makes it difficult to work within the time frames and the process of post mortem makes the body unsuitable for embalming and/or donation.

Size and weight

There are some physical practicality reasons where it cannot be possible to accept a donor. Two of these are size and weight. Either end of the spectrum makes it more unlikely that a donor will be accepted. If a donor is too skinny (technically termed emaciated) there is little to dissect and it is harder for the anatomy to be understood. Cancer treatments and dementia can cause a patient to become too thin. If the individual is obese (roughly anyone over a 100kg) this can be a health and safety problem when it comes to moving the donor. There are also weight limits for the tables.

With obesity increasing in the population this creates different challenges for doctors. Certain specialist courses require donors who are obese as this reflects the reality of the anatomy and surgical situation these doctors must work with. Despite the rise in obesity, emaciation (abnormally thin) is a more common reason for declining a donation.

With regard to height, a short stature is less of a problem, but if a donor is too tall for our tables, sadly they cannot be accepted.

I can honestly promise that we do our utmost to take an individual knowing it was their wishes. I also know it is very hard on the family if we cannot accept a donation. There are times when I have had to break this news and I understand their feelings. For some, they have been relieved, for others, shattered as they had never considered any other options and are not sure what the person would have wanted as a second choice. I also understand how difficult it must be for relatives when we accept a donation to have us asking questions but this is necessary for the process to be concluded successfully.

While everything is done to confirm a donation and commence the preservation process, over the past 20 years there have been some cases when a donation has been accepted because the next of kin or doctors have not disclosed the whole truth.

Case 1.

The family so badly wanted us to have the donation that they blatantly lied about the individual. In this case, the individual had several deformities. I cannot say more to protect anonymity but let's say they would have easily been known in the community due to the obvious nature of their deformity. Don't get me wrong, I understand why they thought the donation would be wanted, if they had been honest it still might have been possible to accept the donation. I am sure the person concerned probably wanted us to use themselves as an example of this condition. But as the information was withheld by the family, nothing was known of it. The acceptance of the donation was based on false information. On arrival, the donor was taken out of the body bag and the extent of the deformity became obvious. The donor did prove difficult to embalm and on dissection had some very interesting pathology. It was interesting for us as academics and for students, but they could not be used for the main purpose that was required. They were cremated after a year and were not really studied as they would have liked to have been, which I think is sad.

Case 2.
The family really wanted their relative to come to a medical school and they had communicated this to the doctor dealing with the death. The doctor had assured them the donation would be accepted. The donor was accepted on the information provided by the doctor. However, at the commencement of embalming it became clear that the individual had a range of conditions that made them unsuitable. These would have been known and obvious to the doctor treating them and who signed the death certificate. They had been accepted based on incorrect information provided by the doctor. The technical team had to continue as best they could, and as predicted the donor did not embalm very well and started to decompose. They were cremated in line with the donors wishes shortly afterwards.

Case 3.
As you may have guessed by now in order for me to undertake my role daily I can become quite desensitized to things. One that did shock me was the information that the next donor had jaundice and had turned a little green during the embalming process. This was an understatement. Their jaundice had reacted with the embalming chemicals and had turned the donor very green. The donation was used to make an amazing face and neck dissection to show the details of the intricate nerves, and students do ask about the colour. If anything, it is a further learning opportunity. Following this, an individual would now be declined if they had severe jaundice.

Case 4.
An individual had donated their body and subsequently after death the family had duly contacted the office. The details of the donation had been taken and the donor had been accepted. Arrangements had been made for the funeral services to collect the body. When the funeral

services got there, they found the donor lying on her side with her legs bent up. Unfortunately, rigor mortis had set in and the funeral services called the office for advice. Through a very difficult conversation the family were informed that sadly it was now not possible for the donation to continue. The position of the body would have made it very difficult to embalm.

If you have a question about a condition and if this might affect your ability to donate or be accepted, please contact your nearest medical school (details at the back of this book). I also recommend that anyone who donates also discusses with the next of kin what they would like to happen if donation is not possible. Usually, the family continue with a cremation or burial.

Preserving a donor

After receiving and confirming the details of the individual, the donor is undressed, washed and their hair is shaved off. This is always a sad part for me as the recent dead look so lifeless, really they do - I know that sounds strange. They look peaceful in their night gown or clothes but cold and sunken. When the process begins, they turn from a donor into a cadaver, or, if then cut into parts, a prosection or a specimen. The donor is given a unique number and removed of any other identity.

Unless the cadaver is to be used for a method called *'Fresh Frozen'* (which I will explain further), the cadaver needs to be embalmed to stop the body from decomposing.

What happens now depends on the different techniques of embalming used.

Traditional embalming
In traditional embalming a mixture of formaldehyde and alcohol is used. To embalm, a small cut is made in an artery. The most commonly used is either the carotid artery in the neck or the femoral artery in the groin. A cannula (small tube) is inserted and is connected to a system that contains the embalming fluid. The fluid is then left to either naturally move around the body, (gravity fed) or is given help with the aid of a pressure pump. The formaldehyde acts to fix the tissue, so it does not decompose. The body will then be rotated to help move the embalming fluid around and to ensure the whole body is *'fixed'*. The term fixed refers to the tissues of the body being stopped from decomposing. The

body is then left to rest for a while, perhaps a couple of months. This resting ensures the tissues are fixed and that the fluid has permeated through the body. At times, due to some conditions within the body (for example narrowing of the arteries) it can be difficult to embalm the hands and feet. If this is the case then these areas are injected directly with formaldehyde. Traditional embalming makes the body tissues harder and not very moveable, so it is important to have the body in the position you will need it in.

Soft Fix

Newer methods called *'soft fixing'* or *'Thiel'* make the tissue more lifelike. The body is still embalmed but with a different fluid mix. The body is then submerged into a liquid for three months. After submerging the body, it is *'fixed'* so it will not decompose but it is still soft and pliable, thus much more like real life. This type of preservation is helpful for certain groups, for example surgeons who can undertake mock operations with much more lifelike precision. Submerging tanks can house up to four donors at any one time. Inside the tank is a four-cage structure. Two donors are in the lower two cages and two in the upper cages. The mechanism lifts the main cage in and out allowing the fluid to drain away. One reason for the cage system is that when you submerge a donor they float so you must have a boundary all the way round.

Fresh Frozen

For some donors, no fixing is needed as they will be used as *'Fresh Frozen'*. While this might sound like I have made this term up, this is what the sector calls it and it is exactly as it sounds. The method of preservation is simply a cold temperature. The body is placed into a freezer and then the donor is defrosted when needed, this gives the advantage of the tissue being as close to lifelike as possible. Fresh frozen is mostly used for training consultants in surgery, anaesthetics, radiology and A&E, where they need to practice and develop techniques on tissue that is as lifelike as possible for surgical simulation. The use of fresh frozen also permits the tools or implants involved in surgery to be developed. Fresh frozen is the most *'expensive'* use of a donor, because re-freezing is not always possible and the surgery destroys that part of the body that means that it cannot be used by another surgeon. Therefore, for fresh frozen the body is often cut into regions to enable as much to be used as possible without being wasteful.

Plastination

The other use of donor bodies that you might have heard of is plastination. This type of fixation involves replacing the body fluid and fat with a plastic resin. The famous example of this is the Body Worlds exhibition established in 1993 by Dr. Gunther Von Hagens. Plastination as a technique is sometimes used for teaching, but be rest assured a donor would not end up in an exhibition like Body Worlds unless they have specifically donated their body to the Body Worlds programme (www.bodyworlds.com). Their website states that they have plastinated over a thousand donors that have come from 33 countries.

Similar to plastination is sheet silicone where a body part is placed into silicone and cut into 1.5mm slices. This is done to mimic the views of anatomy that are seen through CT or MRI scans.

Storage of donors

The storage of donors depends on the method of preservation as described above. If a donor has been embalmed using formaldehyde they can be stored in a variety of ways.

Donors do not need to be refrigerated. The donors that are worked on by medical students can remain in the room at a controlled slightly lower than normal temperature for a couple of years. The donors are stored on tables with a slightly damp cloth and then a white plastic sheet covering them and tucked in around the body. Some institutions use body bags instead of a sheet. Other institutions have tables with metal covers that are simply placed over the donor. Some donors are stored in a body fridge system (Figure 5). Another storage option is a rack system (Figure 6) that looks very much like the inside of a body fridge that you might see on a TV show but with no refrigeration.

If a donor is made into prosections (body parts) these are stored in a different way. Each institution has their own preference for how prosections are stored. Some store prosections on trays in a body fridge. They might store all the prosections they need for a teaching class on one tray or they might store prosections of similar regions, such as all lower legs together on one tray. Prosections are always labelled so they can be traced back via systems (including barcoding) to the donor. Prosections are stored with cloths between them or in their own bags. Some institutions use a submersion system for storage so a prosection will be stored in a tank of fluid.

There is a need to care for donors when they are being stored. An Anatomy Technician is responsible for this. They check many components such as; fluid levels, identity labels, wear from use and for any signs of mould.

Figure 5. Body fridges

Figure 6. Body rack

You may not be aware, but anatomy laboratories are also often on emergency services contingency plans in the event of a local provision need. For example, in the event of a major disaster I could move some of our donors out of full body fridge space and free up space for the local need temporarily. Of course, for this to happen there would need to be quick intervention from licencing authorities. There is also often a memorandum of understanding between Anatomy departments so that if one school was unable to store donors and teach students due to a major emergency then another school would assist as best as they could. Also, the fire and police services hold information that a building such as ours contains donor bodies and the location and type of chemicals being stored.

Supply and demand of donors

Supply and demand for donations is difficult to balance. Medical teaching runs in set patterns within the year. In addition courses for surgeons, et cetera, run on a need basis. Therefore it is not possible to predict with certainty how many donors will be needed in the next 12 months. At the same time, of course, it is not possible to predict that donors will die at a certain point. This makes supply and demand quite a challenge.

Time from donation to death

For years, the demand has been increasing with more medical and allied health students needing to learn anatomy, coupled with at times fewer people donating their body. The London Anatomy Office receives around 3,000 consent forms returned each year. But of course, it may be a number of years before the donor actually dies. It used to be that there were some 40-50 years between when an individual would register the donation and when they died. In recent years the time between donation and death has decreased because individuals with a terminal diagnosis are deciding to donate. I can speculate this may be because there are more individuals with terminal conditions such as cancer and awareness of choices for individuals with terminal illness has also improved. It is now possible that the time from donation to death is very varied and can be years, months, weeks and even days.

There is also a change in the demographics of donors. Traditionally donors would be between 60-90 at the time of death but this age range is expanding. Within London, the youngest donor died aged 35. The youngest donor I have personally worked on was 46 when they died. The record stood for many years for the oldest donor at 103 when they died, then 104 and now it is 106.

Seasonal variations

There are often fluctuations in deaths rates over the year. It can be that nine donors die on the same day and the London Anatomy office is very busy or that no one dies for two or three days. Please don't think when the office is quiet there is little to do - donation secretaries (bequeathal officers) wouldn't be pleased with me for suggesting that! They are always busy managing the documentation and arranging funeral services. There is a seasonal trend in donations, often based on the weather, so this has to be managed. A cold snap or heat wave is likely to increase the number of donors who die, as those with frailty, COPD, pneumonia et cetera, are more likely to die when there are extremes of temperature. Body donation is also susceptible to global healthcare trends, such as a flu epidemic. In the Winter of 2017, there were many cases of influenza. Together with cold weather in early spring there was an increase in the number of individuals on the donation register dying, to the point that many medical schools were full. When I say full, I simply mean that there is not enough space to respectfully embalm and store a donation.

Looking at supply and demand on a wider national scale, the London Anatomy office has been looking at supplying other medical schools as far away as Scotland. This was brought about by the Royal College of Surgeons England, based in London, closing for refurbishment for several years. This was going to potentially leave around 100 donations available to other medical schools. As a community, anatomists try not to turn donations away, and always try to fulfil donors wishes.

Loans

As mentioned, the Human Tissue Authority has a set postcode system in place for donations. However, there are occasions when a donor will be accepted to a medical school, but their whole body or parts can be loaned to another medical school. This occurs when there is a need that cannot be met locally. I will give you an example:

The University of Oxford could not obtain several brains it needed for a neurosurgical course. My equivalent there approached me and asked if I had any brains I could loan. As it happened I had. It was October and I had just removed many brains from donors in the dissection class for second year medical students. Some brains had already been used by medical students in teaching but there were a few I was going to use later in the year. The team could remove more brains between now and then. I hence agreed to loan The University of Oxford 10 brains for two months. The brains were packaged up in locked containers and a named person on their HTA licence drove them to Oxford. The brains were then used as planned to help neurosurgeons understand more of the anatomy and to help them plan a new type of neurosurgery. The brains were returned to BSMS a month later and were reunited with their body. Just so you know, there are standard operating procedures in place for transport of human material, just in-case there is an accident or a vehicle breakdown.

Import
There are times when the supply in the United Kingdom cannot match the demand. This is usually for postgraduate surgical training, when a group of surgeons are trialling a new technique and wish to undertake a procedure several times. Their preference to do this is for fresh frozen. Trying to get 20 fresh frozen heads in for a specific date is difficult. A previous solution was to look to companies in the United States.

The United States, currently has different rules and regulations to the United Kingdom. Their regulations vary across different states, where in some it is legal for the unclaimed dead and the dead from prisons to be used for anatomy. Donations are also taken from family members (second person consent) as well as donations from individuals themselves (first person consent). Because the law in the United Kingdom only permits donations via first person (i.e. they donated their own body in sound mind) this is the only donation that can be imported. Before the laws changed it was likely that body parts from the unclaimed dead through these private companies did enter the United Kingdom for surgical training.

When I know what an upcoming surgical course requires, such as 30 feet or 10 shoulders, I first see if this can be sourced from the local donation programme. It has only been over the past year (2018) that BSMS has been able to use United Kingdom based body donations to fulfil all of our surgical courses. This has been aided by a repository centre at Nottingham. Here donors are frozen and stored to later be loaned to United Kingdom medical schools. If supply meant it was not possible then either myself or the course organiser place an order with a company in the United States. In 2014, BSMS imported 234 body parts. Over subsequent years this decreased to 128, 52 and 24 in 2017. The decrease was due to being able to source donations from within the United Kingdom.

Due to logistical reasons of storage I have only imported donated body parts (specimens). These are tested for a series of known transmissible diseases such as hepatitis, active TB and HIV. The body parts are packaged and sent in the hold of a plane across the Atlantic. For me they land at London Gatwick Airport and are then picked up by a special courier and delivered directly to the Anatomy department. However, a few times the couriers did leave them with University stores or the school office! Once the donor specimens have been received, the records are checked to ensure they match the documentation previously sent over by the company. The donation is supposed to be sent to us frozen but so many factors affected this, such as flight delays, and sometimes the donation has become fully defrosted on arrival.

If the donation is not needed for a few weeks they are placed in the freezer until required. The donor would be defrosted over hours or days depending on their size. To begin with it was difficult to work out the defrost times. This was overcome simply by applying our own knowledge of defrosting frozen food in our own home freezer, which works rather well.

It is sad that currently the only way to dispose of imported donated body parts is via clinical incineration. They cannot be cremated as they did not die in the United Kingdom and hence do not have the correct forms. It is not as simple as just being sent an extra form. In the cases of heads, I have returned these back to the United States. An increase in fresh frozen facilities in the United Kingdom will hopefully mean that soon there will be no need to import donated body parts.

When it doesn't quite go to plan
A United States company once sent some specimens with donation numbers that did not match the donor details on the system. I immediately contacted the company straight away and queried this. It turned out they had sent us the wrong ones. They had sent donor parts from non-first person consenting individuals that I was not able to accept under the HTA licence conditions in the United Kingdom. The company initially said they wouldn't take them back. I explained I could not accept them and would not break the law and calmly insisted that they had to fly them back. After a few exchanges they agreed and the donor parts were temporarily with me for a few hours before being turned around and put back on a plane to return to the United States.

Another time, the technician was waiting for a delivery of feet. They were informed that there was a delay at customs (I wouldn't recommend unwrapping that box!). Eventually the feet arrived at the university at 10 p.m. on a Friday evening.

There was another occasion when eight legs cut at the level of the inguinal ligament (groin) had been requested. After delivery, it became obvious that these were the correct eight lower limbs but that it wasn't just the lower limb. These legs were attached to the hip and the pelvis. It then became clear that this was going to be a difficult job to fit them all in our upright -20°C freezers (Figure 7). Think of your big family upright fridge at home, only it gets colder and has sensors that dial out to an emergency phone if the temperature drops above/below the set temperature. It was difficult to work out how to place these donor parts in the freezer. It really was like Jenga or twister as the technicians placed and then turned around each leg to get them all in. They had to hold the specimens in the freezer and quickly move their arms out of the way to shut the door. It worked but only just! At one point, the technical team were seriously considering getting the saw out and sawing a few into two parts to get them in the freezer.

On another occasion, the company informed the Prosector that the specimens would be frozen and hence could be left out at room temperature to defrost over the weekend for a surgical course on a Monday. When the donor body parts arrived, they were not frozen! This would have been okay if there was space in the freezer, but our freezers were full. The only solution was to bring our emergency freezer over from another building, get it down to fridge temperature and put the donor parts in there over the weekend. There was an emergency freezer in another building in case of loss of power to ours. However, it is not easy to move these freezers.

Figure 7. Top part of one body part freezer

Solutions

So, what could be done about under-supply? Many have suggested an opt out system, like the one that has been adopted in Wales for organ donation. I feel though this is probably not needed for anatomy, as while there are dips in supply numbers, it is never substantial enough to warrant a significant change in law. One issue for the United Kingdom is that there is no central repository that can store donated bodies and parts. If there was, this would help, especially in the use of fresh frozen donated parts.

I personally think that society has made death very clinical and removed. I wonder if through improved education and information about death and the choices individuals have at a much earlier stage individuals will be better informed. Advertising body donation has not really been done by the regulatory bodies, compared to organ donation and carrying donor cards which is well established and understood by the public. However, attitudes are changing and over the past few years I have received more and more requests from journalists who are writing about the issue. The result could be more people donating their body. Acknowledging the generous gift of donors in the press might be a way to say '*Thank you*' and to raise awareness of this option.

The other option would be to widen the scope of the organ donation system to include anatomy and specific research banks (for example brain banks). This might make one large and complex system. It would likely result in the sector having too many donations, that in turn may mean turning down more donations. This would not be acceptable as this could place extra distress on families at a very difficult time.

My solution to this would be to encourage the government to help set up a national '*fresh frozen*' centre so that supply and demand can be improved on a national basis so that no donations are turned down. If this was in place anatomy departments would not have to import any body parts from overseas.

Body donation laws

The history of body donation has not been without it issues. In the seventeenth and eighteenth century, the Plague and battlefield injuries led to a drive to improve health through medicine and surgery. This in turn led to the increase in the need for human bodies to be studied by dissection, leading to bodies being procured rather than donated! A legal supply existed but was limited to a couple of bodies a year through the Murders Act of 1752. This Act gave anatomy rooms the bodies of people who had committed murder and had been hanged for it. As demand outstretched supply, grave robbers (also known as resurrectionists) removed the bodies of the deceased to supply medical schools. Interestingly, the act of removing the body from a grave was not against the law but it was against the law to steal grave goods.

Doctors and scientists also turned to grave robbing to locate their next subject. Famous examples include Andreas Vesalius and William and John Hunter. Andreas Vesalius was a 16th century anatomist, often referred to as the founder of modern human anatomy, via his book 'De humani corporis fabrica'. William Hunter was a 17th century anatomist and physician. His brother John was a famous surgeon. The Hunterian Museum at the Royal College of Surgeons England still contains his collection of anatomical specimens. Two notable figures in history - Burke and Hare - took to murdering subjects to supply the anatomy teaching room of Robert Knox in Edinburgh.

Grave robbing

Interfering with a grave was a misdemeanour punishable by a fine or imprisonment but authorities tended to ignore it. As it became more prevalent grave robing became unacceptable. In 1832, the first Anatomy Act was created and this permitted licenced anatomists to take unclaimed bodies from institutions where individuals had been kept at a cost to the government, such as the local workhouses. Records show that in 1833 only 44 bodies were donated, but around 500 were sourced from the local workhouses. The number of bodies from the workhouses decreased over time and in 1850 records show that less than 300 bodies for anatomy came from workhouses. The number of bodies needed was high for the ratio of doctors in training because of the limited preservation techniques. Medical students would have only days to work on one body before decomposition made it unsuitable. In the late eighteenth century chemicals, such as Phenol and Formaldehyde, were created and their ability to *'fix'* tissue proved them to be an effective method of stopping decomposition. Bodies were then embalmed with these chemicals, giving students a longer amount of time to study the anatomy and fewer donor bodies were subsequently required.

The use of unclaimed bodies stopped in the United Kingdom after the first world war but sadly it continues in many countries. It was only in 2016 that the eight medical schools in New York said they would no longer accept the bodies of the unclaimed as cadavers. This is not an exhaustive list but in South Africa, Nigeria, Bangladesh, Brazil and India the use of unclaimed bodies is legal. I talk more about my experiences of this later (Chapter 6).

Anatomy Act 1984
The Anatomy Act was redefined in 1984. It was designed and presided over by Her Majesty's Inspector of Anatomy. Perhaps one strange thing about the Act was that a person or a next of kin could donate your body on their say so (second person consent). When speaking to a relative who was phoning to say their Father/Mother had passed away, the relatives often said things like *'he/she would have wanted this'*, you could sense them nodding on the telephone line. Some individuals might have genuinely wanted to donate their body on their death, but it was often felt that there might have been an alternative motive, i.e. it was free and saved on funeral expenses (as the medical school cover costs). You might consider that harsh, but some next of kin just said so, and why not? Dying is an expensive business. In 2017, Brighton and Sussex Medical School spent £26,000 on funeral expenses for donated cadavers.

I was awarded my Anatomy Act 1984 licence in 2003, just before the law changed in 2004. It is the only certificate I have on display at home in the study. I like the official cresting and the fact that it is valid until I am 70 or until I leave University of Southampton (I have!).

Human Tissue Act 2004
With the aftermath of the Bristol and Alder Hey scandals, where it was found that children's organs had been retained without consent, the law changed and from 2005, the Human Tissue Authority (HTA) was established to regulate the Human Tissue Act 2004. Consent is at the centre of the law and only individuals can donate their bodies. The change in regulations also added clarity to the activity of practicing surgical procedures on donated bodies which was a grey area in the 1984 law. In 2008, the number of bodies accepted in the United Kingdom had climbed to around 900.

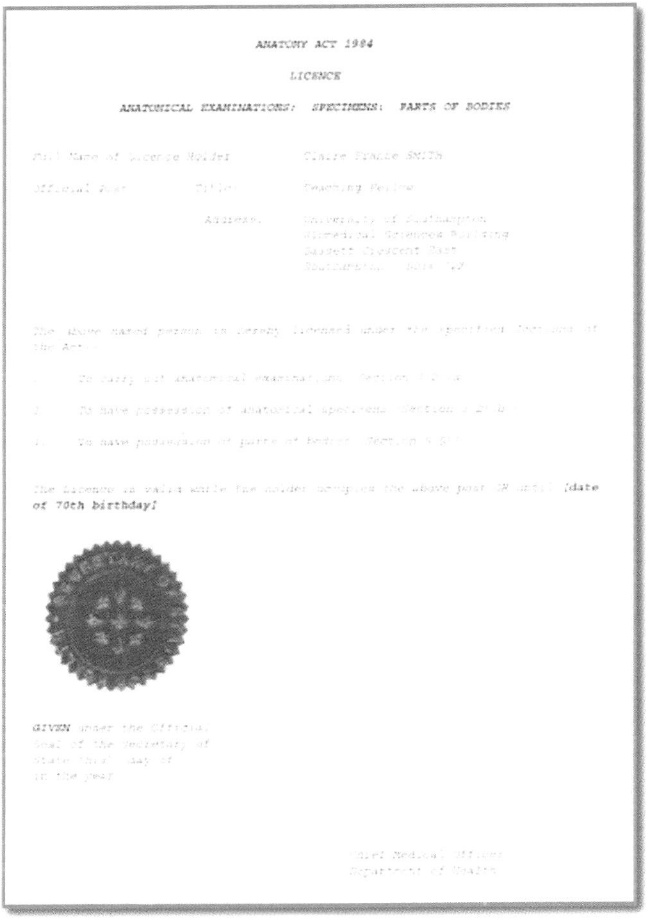

Figure 8. Anatomy Act certificate.

A personal experience of body donation

Of course, sometimes there is a personal level of involvement. On my grandfather's side of the family there was a family member who lived near Norwich, East Anglia. Knowing I worked for the medical school in Southampton they asked me about how they would donate their body. This was quite simple in that I contacted their nearest medical school (University of East Anglia) and arranged for them to send out the relevant paperwork. My concern, in this instance, was that it could look like I was trying to recruit and that would be unethical. The situation was further compounded when the relative's brother and sister in-law also chose to donate. They live in the New Forest and since donation is arranged by postcode, this meant that their local medical school was the one I was working at. I explained this to my relatives and walked four desks along to the local bequeathal officer. I said nothing more to encourage or discourage the donation, but because of the relationship it felt strange. They are still alive so who knows if they will end up in my old anatomy lab.

What then happened pushed my own boundaries. My grandfather had his 92nd birthday party and invited relatives. You can probably guess where this is going - it was the relatives who had donated their body. This caused my mind to spin. Firstly, I knew it was them and had to sit next to them and engage in polite conversation about their life. I have never had to meet a potential donor, let alone have Sunday lunch with them and engage in pre-Christmas jollities (his birthday was in December). It was hard to look at their face and eyes, their smile without thinking of them on a dissection table with the colour drained from their face looking lifeless, either with their eyes closed or staring blankly towards an aspect of the room. It made me think, could I cut them up? Could I be in the same room with them? Where were my boundaries?

But would I have to? Their local medical school was Southampton and there is no guarantee that they will be accepted. However, knowing their medical history it is looking likely. If I had stayed working at Southampton and that had been the case I would have paid to have them transported to Bristol or a London school so I could enable them to fulfil their wish. It is also possible that if Southampton was full they could be referred to the London area which means they could come to me. If this occurred I would not take them. However, it is not always me who makes the call to say yes to accepting a donor. I have a great team who are trained to make such decisions. It might simply be that I am giving a lecture or in a meeting across at the hospital site when the call comes in. Information such as name, date, location and cause of death is received to begin with, so they might not think any differently about accepting this donor. At the same time, these relatives might not have contacted my mother yet so it is a real possibility. While writing this, I mentally note to list their names somewhere so the team know.

There is no training for this, I know every time I uncover a donor and see their face that they were a person, that never goes and things like this remind me that they would have sat and had Sunday lunch too.

Chapter 3. The Dissecting Room (DR)

Now you have read about what happens to a donor I am going to walk you through the Dissecting Room (DR). The term DR has been described as a faceless abbreviation. Some call it the Anatomy Laboratory, Dissecting Laboratory or the Morphology Laboratory. Others have tried to jazz it up a bit, examples include Centre for Learning Anatomical Sciences (CLAS), Facility for Learning Anatomy Morphology and Embryology (FLAME). No matter what it is called, it is the physical space licensed for the activity of Anatomical Examination, i.e. where examination of donated dead human bodies occurs.

While talking terminology, donors who donate their bodies are often referred to as *'cadavers'*. Anatomists tend to talk about donors when the donation is being offered and at the end of the process. The term cadaver is used when talking about the actual body or body part in a laboratory/DR. I might say to a colleague *'donor number 123 is due to be transferred to us today'* but during a teaching session to students in the DR *'cadaver number 12 has a great example of an aortic aneurysm'*.

The entrance door to the Anatomy Laboratory has a notice that informs individuals they are entering a space governed by the Human Tissue Act. There is a piece of artwork on the wall that was made by a student before I arrived. I still am not sure if I like it or not, so it has remained there. The artwork includes a mirror so often people look at this. Entry into the anatomy laboratory is via a secure chip in a wristband and a passcode. There is CCTV in operation. Occasionally I like to watch strangers on the CCTV screen. They have a good look at the outside of the door, read the door sign and look at the artwork. What is it about a mirror that means that people must check something of themselves in it? Teeth, hair, make up, et cetera, I also like walking out of the door when non-medical students are hanging around in the corridor, they always look shocked that such a secure door has opened.

While writing this the DR at BSMS is in the processes of having an upgrade and an extension to the facility to accommodate an increase in medical student numbers. For now, I will describe it as it currently is. The main DR and preparation space will all remain the same. The expansion will change two adjacent teaching rooms into a second DR. This will be achieved by knocking a wall down to create either a large space that will hold 130 students or three spaces that will hold 70, 30 and 30 students. This arrangement will enable a greater degree of flexibility so that consecutive teaching sessions can occur for students and surgeons. All DRs have some type of changing room space for gowns; a main space where the teaching occurs; a preparation room and an office.

The changing room

When you go through the door you then come into the changing room. It is square with benches and hanging space. Hanging up are 70 surgical gowns, exactly like the ones used by surgeons in operating theatres but are not sterile (Figure 9). Even if a non-medical student got a passing glance inside while one of us was walking through the door they would only see green gowns hanging up. You need to put on a gown that means your arms go in towards the front and you turn around to do it up. You then need to put on some gloves. If you're not wearing glasses for vision correction you pick up a pair of protective eye visors. These have different colour plastic rims and there is always a fight for the pink ones (I don't know why!).

When students first start to use the DR the procedure of gowning and gloving up takes quite a while but over the first term students naturally become quicker. In the changing room space, you leave everything - your phone, bag, bottles of water, et cetera, as nothing is permitted into the main laboratory. All users of the DR must wear sensible shoes and all long hair must be tied back. This is not a place for fashion - it really is not very nice when your hair falls into an abdominal cavity! Students are required to not wear flip flops or high heels. It does make me smile that some students wear fashionable and expensive footwear in the laboratory. The floor in the laboratory often has spills, and bits of fat or body fluids can easily spill onto shoes so I always recommend that a cheap pair of trainers are worn.

Figure 9. One section of the changing room

The teaching laboratory

Once you are ready, you then go through a door and into the main laboratory. It is a light room with a main projector screen and control panel at one end. The room is quite like an operating theatre, it has that sterile and harsh feel. The walls are light and the floor is vinyl that goes up the walls, making it easy to clean. On the right is a row of handwashing sinks. The room is light, partly because of the lights but also the windows at the end of the DR are real windows and we have an amazing view over the South Downs. I really like teaching and being able to glance up and feel the outside. In spring, I can look out and see the light bouncing off the green shoots on the trees. In summer, I can see the flag of the University Senate during *'Pride'* with the colours moving in the wind. In autumn, the fading light is replaced quite early with the yellow glow of university lights. In winter, darker hours just reflect the bright lights of the DR and the contrast between such a light space and the dark outsides intensifies. All other windows in the DR are made with frosted glass so light comes in but you cannot see in or out. A little story goes that when the DR was built and the HTA inspectors visited they mentioned they were concerned that a low flying aircraft could see in. The founding Professor quickly pointed out that if anyone was in a plane so close to this building, that seeing some dead bodies was the least of their worries!

On the window sill I like to place large anatomy models, of maybe a head or a heart, so that when it is dark outside you can see the silhouette of a body shape from the outside. It is also good storage! At Halloween time, I ensure a large plastic skull is placed on one of these!

Below is the best picture I can use to show the teaching laboratory (Figure 10). The reason why you cannot see a lot of detail is to ensure that I do not show you anything that contains human material. Just to the right of the picture is the wall that will get knocked down to expand into the room next door.

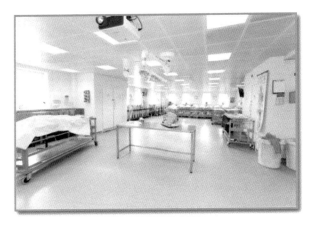

Figure 10. The teaching room

The ceiling is lined with specialist air management systems that means that the air in the DR is changed ten times an hour. There are also down posts of electrical sockets that enable surgical instruments to be plugged in without trailing cables. A large operating theatre light looms from the ceiling at the front. It gives off a bright light lined with red light cells that make it feel quite futuristic.

Around the room are 10 plastic skeletons. These are always used by students and staff and as a result are always *'sticky'* to touch. There is also a range of real skeletons that hang from stands. It is common to walk in and find the plastic skeletons dancing or in a pose with their arms around each other as if posing for a picture. The students and junior doctors must do this. I really don't mind.

Museum pots
Around the room are shelves that contain museum pots. Museum pots are jars or similar glass pots that contain human parts. Many of these are historical, with a number being over a hundred years old. Some are a specialist dissection of a difficult region, such as the arteries in the hand.

Others are of pathology, so examples of what has gone wrong in the body, for example a brain that has undergone a stroke. These pots are very precious and it takes special care from anatomy technicians to make them and keep them in good order. Some of the pots are very special as they contain examples of disease that would be difficult to see today. This is often because modern medicine has changed and things would not be allowed to get to that stage. One example is a kidney with lots of cysts on it. There are so many that this organ that is normally 10-12cm in length is now 30cm and looks much more like a lung with large bubbles in it. The pots give the room a historical feeling as body parts remain in them for many years.

Body tables

In the centre of the room are nine tables laid out in three rows of three (these have been pushed to the back in Figure 10). Each table has two levels on it (this can be seen on the table on the left-hand side of the picture) and will usually have a cadaver on each level. This clever design that was made specifically for us means that 18 cadavers can be easily stored. Students work on the cadaver that is on the top level. Then when there is a need to switch them over the system is counter-weighted so with two people it is possible to rotate the levels so that body that was on the lower level is now on top. This can occur two times a day based on teaching need. The difficult bit is rotating the table when you only have one donor on it. You slide the cadaver over to the table but then there is no weight on the lower level so it will just spin round in a dangerous way. I did ask one of team (since no one volunteered) to lie down on the lower level to provide the bottom counter weight! The better solution is to place sandbags on the lower level as we rotate it so the empty lower level is now on the top and a cadaver can be slid onto it.

Each cadaver is assigned a black box on wheels. This box is very much like a tool box from a known DIY retailer. When the donor is being dissected the black box is located at the head end of the table. The box is labelled with the donor and table number. This is always checked before use. The box contains anything that is removed from the cadaver. This includes every single piece of hair, fat, tissue, et cetera. All removed material is placed in a bag that remains inside the black box until eventually it is time to place the cadaver in their coffin. When the brain is removed, it is also placed in the black box, in a white sealed bucket. When the donor is not being worked on the black boxes are moved to the edge of the room under the shelves.

Washing up

The room, also contains handwashing sinks (these are out of shot on the right-hand side of the picture), that operate hands-free via infrared sensors to reduce the risk of contamination. Instrument washing sinks are on the opposite side of the room and after each teaching session one student from each group is responsible for the washing up. This uses ordinary washing liquid and the student places the clean instruments on blue paper above the sink to air dry. The technical team then collect up the instruments and re-sort them for the next class. If a group of students ever forgets to wash up the consequence is that that team must wash up the entire class of 70 students' instruments at the next session. Once a year this happens as one group forgets and there is always laughter from the other students.

The walls of the DR are decorated in a mix of anatomical posters. I like these, some are a little historical (your classic *'muscle man'* picture), others are focused on a specific region of anatomy, such as the ear, where small details are shown in a larger magnification, others are regulatory information and certificates relating to the Human Tissue Authority. Also placed on the wall four times around the room is a list of the cadavers students are working on. This list simply states the cadaver number, age at death and any medical history. No names or identifiable information are on this list. This list is helpful as when students are working they can check to see if their cadaver had any condition that would show up in that teaching session. Students can also check the list if they are looking for an example of a condition (pneumonia) so they can ensure they visit that table to see that pathology (disease). Seeing the age of death on the list is also a reminder for me of that person. I often think to myself, *'they lived longer or shorter than my father or grandfather, I think of the family members they have left behind'.*

The preparation room

The *'prep room'* is separate to the DR and has a large complex external door system to the outside, through an airlock. The airlock is large enough to hold up to two coffins that means that they can be delivered into this space and the doors to the outside world closed before the corresponding doors to the prep room are opened. This system is designed so that it is not possible for anyone who might be passing on the outside to see inside.

The prep room contains a wall that houses a sixteen-donor fridge system. This fridge system does not only contain full bodies waiting to be studied but is also used for the storage of prosections (body parts). Prosections are parts of a donor that have given specific consent for the medical school to retain to be studied by students after the main body has been cremated, for example an upper limb. Prosections are expertly dissected by a person who holds the title Prosector (Ms. Lydia Carline). Lydia will spend many hours in the prep room working on a prosection, with some such as complex ones of the head can take months to prepare.

There are three tall fridge freezers that are used for storage of fresh frozen parts. These can be set to any temperature down to -20°C. The freezers also contain a dial-out system, so if the temperature increases above a set level the on-call phone holder is notified. This is important in case of a breakdown or if there is a power cut, so that as staff we are alerted and can relocate the body parts to another fridge/freezer before they defrost and decompose.

Across from the freezers is a powerful band saw that has a large rotating blade that moves around above a platform. The band saw deserves respect and a lot of health and safety controls. It can easily cut arms off, heads in half et cetera, which is what it is used for. The saw even goes through metal teeth and plastic dentures (Figure 11). This means using extreme caution and a carefully planned system of clear procedures, protective equipment and safety guards to push body parts through the band saw. If I am being honest I don't really like using it, the consequences of getting it wrong are very real. The band saw is used to slice heads into two parts, often up to 10 heads a year. The heads are frozen first to get a clean line through the middle of the nose! For larger things, for example, to take the head off or to separate the thorax from the abdomen, the technician will use a hand saw.

Some larger medical schools have larger band saws that will slice a whole body or will cut off a head. Lydia and Lucinda will tell you though that often the amount of time it takes to prepare a whole body for the band saw to just remove an arm or head is quite a lot and that it is often quicker to just get a saw and do it by hand. I would like to tell you here that while the laboratory does have some very specialist equipment, hand saws are not one of them. The technician just makes a trip to the local DIY store and buys branded saws. Once they are blunt they are simply disposed of through the clinical waste system.

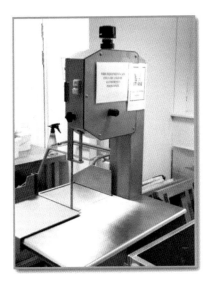

Figure 11. The band saw

Figure 12. The body stack

The last part of the preparation room is the body stack (Figure 12). As supply and demand is not constant there is a need to save up donors for the start of each academic year. Donors are placed on a metal stacking system that can contain up to twelve bodies. These donors are still in a plastic bag and are covered with a white plastic sheet. It is a bespoke system of four storage levels, repeated in three rows. Between each level is enough space for a donor and a gap so air is free to move around the stack. The stack does look a little odd when full as clearly the white plastic cover is draped over the shape of a human body (Figure 12). Each body has a tag on its ear and another around an ankle but you can only see these by removing the plastic sheet and moving the clear plastic bag enough to be able to see through it.

When I look at the body stack I notice the shiny crisp white plastic layer lying over them. It is not creased from use. If you move the white plastic you can see through the clear bag. You can see their donor number and the faces not yet wrapped in muslin cloth because these bodies are not yet ready to be used for teaching. This reminds me very clearly even at a quick glance that these are complete new donors. They are awaiting their first cut by a member of staff in preparing them for the next academic year.

Next to the prep room there is a staff changing room with shower and a toilet. The shower is essential for emergencies, such as a burn from chemicals that requires rinsing. It is also essential when body bits get flicked into your hair or body fluids soak through your scrubs and onto your skin. As showers go it is okay -the Ritz it is not! The changing room is small and a tag system of very quick changes one after another occurs before and after each teaching session. During the teaching session, the changing room is full of smelly shoes, socks and clothes always half hanging up, it really does resemble a rugby club changing room! I am very particular about not letting my clothes fall on the floor, after all the team walk into this room with shoes that have been in the DR.

While talking about clothes, one thing you do find is that naturally the DR is a cold space. At times this is not a problem, such as when it has 70 students in (warm bodies) it soon warms up and can even feel hot. At other times when preparation work is going on outside of teaching it feels quite cold so layers under scrubs are needed. One of the technicians (Lucinda) really feels the cold and she is often found sat at her computer with a hot water bottle warming up. Given that if it was warm the smell would increase and the donors would dry out, I think everyone is in agreement a colder environment and an extra layer is much better!

The DR Office

The DR has a dedicated office with space for five desks. Two are used by the Prosector (Lydia) and Technician (Lucinda) and the rest by junior doctors. When the remaining three desks are in use it is a squeeze and you cannot easily walk past to the changing room. The laboratory office is an environment that is a little strange. It has full windows into the prep room and the body stack, yet the office and the staff that work in it have a food fridge and a clean environment. No gloves or gowns are allowed although scrubs are permitted, so it is usual to walk in and see staff having a cup of tea, an apple or banana when working on a computer, reading a text book or chatting with the window back drop of the body stack. The reason they get a food fridge (before anyone complains) is so that they can store their own drinks and lunch in it without having get changed out of their scrubs and head to the café. They are a sensible lot and if their scrubs are dirty they will change them. Please don't think that Lydia and Lucinda are sat there eating their cheese sandwiches with bits of body stuck to their scrubs! The fridge also contains an essential supply of things like cola that I never normally drink but when teaching for two to three hours, talking continually and moving (some dissecting is hard physical work), the fridge and its contents provide an essential energy refill.

Next to the fridge are two large fire-proofed filing cabinets that are always locked. They contain all the paper records of every donor BSMS has ever had in our care. Also in the office is a large computer system that controls the CCTV and the teaching computer screens and sound system. Go back a few years and DRs didn't have CCTV. When it was brought in there was some resistance to it by some teachers not wanting to be recorded. I feel it is there for the donors and if it catches me occasionally happily skipping in the DR or spending a few minutes looking out the window then so be it!

Figure 13. The DR Office (Lucinda working)

Other Dissecting Rooms

I have described so far, my own dissecting room, a typical one for the UK, but of course I have worked and visited many other around the United Kingdom and in Europe. The old dissecting room at the University of Southampton, Bolderwood Campus was built in the 1960s, in a typical concrete building of the era (it was also known favourably as Bolditz) that has since been demolished. It was located on the first floor above the canteen and bar and I always wondered if the air systems mixed! We really could have a pint at lunch time and dissect in the afternoon. I have fond memories of Bolditz. One year it snowed lots and it had beautiful grounds, full of rhododendron bushes. There was so much snow that the anatomy team went out and used metal trays from the DR as sledges!

Donors would be brought in the back door through a gentle ramp that would then lead into an embalming room. In the centre of the room was a white stone embalming table. A side room contained a large band saw. The dissecting room itself was divided into two by temporary partition boards to separate out areas being used by year one and year two medical students respectively. Off the dissecting room was the laboratory office with three or four desks and filing cabinets.

I was also called to this DR at 3 a.m. one morning. The alarms were going and that the rear door was ajar. Security had called the police and had then called me. I think there was a roster system of who was first call and my name must have been top. The police were informed not to go any further onto licensed premises until I was present. Having quickly got dressed and travelled there the police were sure that the facility had been broken into. They had asked what was in there. I explained there was probably a body on the embalming table and if they went into the main area and preparation space there would be a range of bodies and body parts. The police seemed a bit unnerved and made me go first, so I walked in the dark unsure if a burglar was going to jump out at me. I turned on as many lights as possible and the police searched the area. It was clear that the burglar must have left, possibly on activating the alarm or, maybe, they walked into the first room and saw the dead body lying on the white stone embalming table. The police said the burglar probably thought it was going to be a computer suite, as this was early 2000s and universities were investing in large computer suites for students. I hope the burglar did see the dead body on the embalming table and maybe it made them think again about breaking and entering a medical school!

Figure 14. Me dissecting at University of Southampton (Bolditz)- 2002, traditional white coat, hair up and latex gloves. The curtains behind me were there to help when taking a photograph using traditional film photography.

Later, it was discovered that the main University Campus building at Bolderwood had concrete fatigue. A plan was developed to relocate the DR. There were discussions about where such a sensitive environment should be located. Almost all the biology laboratory space, office space and teaching rooms were going to be relocated to the main university campus. However senior management at the time did not want what was perceived to be a messy and dirty environment on its main campus that was close to residential areas. It was therefore suggested that the DR was relocated to the Southampton General Hospital site. From my perspective, I spent lots of time at the hospital anyway, either teaching or seeing clinicians, so apart from having to pay £50 a month in parking for a space you were only able to use if you arrived at 7.30 a.m. and adding an hour onto my daily commute, I was up for this new environment!

A dissecting room was created. This space had some limits that meant it had a central raised hub that contained body processing and storage. It was such a different height that cadavers had to be passed through a hatch lift system. There is a main DR space and then three rooms that can be separated. As Southampton only taught using prosections, its storage system is slightly different to the one I have described at BSMS. They process donors and then most are made into prosections. The prosections are stored in sealed bags on sliding body trays that contain all the parts for a teaching session, for example a second-year medical school class examining the head looking at the trigeminal nerve that supplies the muscles involved in chewing (mastication), the feeling of sensation over the face and the nerves that supply the teeth. There would be up to twenty heads used for this teaching session. To store them they would all be in their own bag on one shelf.

Other DRs I have worked in or visited range from the very traditional to very modern. Some are in the basement and are located next to a mortuary; some are up on the 11th floor of a tower block. While there are differences across the country and donors can be used for slightly different things based on local need, the fundamental principles (and of course the law that I operate within) is the same. I can honestly say there is no one place I would want a relative to go or not to go. All anatomists care deeply about our donors and treat them with the utmost respect. If you are a future medical/dental/allied health professional student reading this and are wondering who has the best facility, we all do, there is no competition, every medical school works to create a space that is an inspiring and engaging learning environment.

A unique environment

I think you now have a good idea of the space where donors are examined and studied. It really is only when you have students who have never been in this environment before or when you explain to someone not involved in medicine that you realise how specialised it is. I was once in the DR teaching second year biomedical science students. They had lectures on anatomy and this DR session was just two hours to give them the opportunity to see and further learn in context the material they had been studying. I had a prosection station on the heart (a station is a table or area where there are a selection of prosections). At this station; I had a museum pot with a heart with a replacement heart valve in, one isolated heart, a prosection of a donor head and thorax. I was talking through the heart but became aware that on every pause all of the students' eyes were drawn and were scanning over the donor, especially the head. I decided to address the issue directly and learned it was the first part of a dead body they had ever seen. Apart from pathologists, funeral directors and mortuary technicians there cannot be many people who see so many dead bodies. I have not counted, but I can estimate that since starting my journey in anatomy I have worked on thousands of donor bodies.

Chapter 4. What happens to the donor

Irrespective of the preservation method chosen by the institution, a body is donated for a maximum of three years and if stated at consent, body parts are retained for beyond three years. There are many things that a donor can be used for. A donor can be left whole after embalming for medical students to systematically dissect and discover the anatomy. They can be cut up into different parts and dissected into expert dissections that are termed *'prosections'*. Prosections are used to teach medical and allied health professional students as well as trained doctors. The donor will remain whole or as parts and are frozen to be used when defrosted by doctors to further develop their skills.

It is important to explain that a medical school or institution can have a public display HTA licence, that allows members of the public to see anatomical specimens and body parts where the donor has given specific consent for public display. If this is not asked about on the donation form, it means that the institution does not have a licence for such activity and hence your body will only be used to train medical, allied healthcare professionals and science students for example, a student training to be a doctor, a nurse or an anatomist. At times the *'Designated Individual'* (the person named on an HTA licence who has a statutory obligation to ensure compliance with the Human Tissue Act) can also grant permission for other individuals to observe donor bodies for example in the training of medical artists or medical engineers.

The Grand Reveal

Before anatomy teaching begins, there is for every student, no matter if they are going to be working on dissection or prosection, the *'grand reveal'* and will remember vividly as very likely the first time they see a dead body.

The grand reveal is where students lift back the plastic covering and the slightly damp cloth that covers their donor or prosected part for the first time. I do feel this time is even more pronounced when it is a full cadaver. There is something about the classic body shape lying underneath a covering.

Students undertake this uncovering slowly and with trepidation. They peel back the cover and expose the thorax, arms and abdomen. The heads of the cadavers remain wrapped by a separate cloth under the main covering. Students normally take a few minutes to just look at the cadaver and take it all in. It is around this time that as a teacher I then help students to focus on the task and turn it back to the anatomy they are seeking to understand. Some students have a need to see further and see the whole body, this is fine, they can just pull the covers back to the level of the feet. The only reason the covers are not completely removed, is just space. I explain to students that when they are working on the cadaver that they will only uncover what they need to. This is to stop the cadaver from drying out. For example, if they are working on the legs then the lower half of the cover is lifted and folded on top of the abdomen, so that the pelvis, abdomen, thorax and head remain covered.

During the same session, I ensure I visit each group and undertake two tasks. Task one is to show them how to uncover the head of a cadaver if required. Some students feel it helps them to understand the reality that this is indeed a person and it also helps them to understand the gift of donation. The students undertake this themselves and pause for a few minutes just looking at their donor. I feel it is important that they can see and understand this was a person who once cried and laughed like all of us. After this the head is recovered with a cloth, it remains covered during other sessions.

The second task is to check with the student group whether they wish to know the first name of their cadaver or if they wish to assign a respectful name. I feel this is important too as it keeps the cadaver as a person. I will not permit any fun or inappropriate names. Most groups decide to know their donors first name and I give them this. Students are also able to find out the age at death and the cause of death. Students are not permitted to know any further information about the donor.

Fainting in the DR

Every year a small number of students find the DR environment too much to cope with on their first visit. They can feel sick and sometimes will faint. Sometimes there may be no first-year students fainting at all, at other times it will be several within a short space of time. For some students this is expected, they tell me that they have always fainted easily.

For others (often large men) it can be a total shock. All teaching and technical staff are trained in first aid and this is often called upon. Both Lydia and Lucinda are great at looking after students who feel unwell or do faint. I will often find Lucinda sat on the changing room floor between a couple of students who are lying down, talking to them and helping them to feel physically and emotionally better. For students who faint the best thing is to get them into the changing room and on the floor before they faint. You can sometimes spot them before they go; their face goes very pale and you can intercept quickly. At other times, there is no time to get them out but you can catch them and manage to get them onto the floor safely. There are two anecdotes I can think of that were slightly more dramatic.

Year 1 student

It was a first-year practical session. Our fainting radars were active and there had already been one student who had succumbed. The session was continuing and I was standing at the front middle table. Out of the corner of my eye I saw a tall male student heading towards the exit not looking great. I turned to check on him and as I did he fainted and fell forward. As he fell he banged the front of his head on the phone that is mounted next to the exit door. This force then pushed him backwards and he fell, knocking the back of his head on the floor. My hands and those of my team were split seconds behind as I tried to catch him. We quickly got him into the recovery position and he regained consciousness. The student was looked after and it was divulged that he had not slept or eaten for 24 hours due to an essay deadline. He was really surprised he had fainted and had no insight into one of the duties of a doctor that is to look after yourself before you can effectively look after patients.

Year 2 student

The first was slightly unusual in that it was well into the academic year, when our normal window of looking for potential fainting students had well passed. The student was in the middle of the session and the session was going well. Suddenly there was a loud bang and we quickly became aware of a commotion by the washing instrument sink. A student was lying on the floor beside the metal sinks. I got them into the recovery position and checked their breathing and pulse, they were okay. They had fainted and had bashed their head on the metal sink as they went down. They were unconscious for a while and were slow to recover so Lucinda called the university emergency system. The student ended up going to hospital and having an MRI scan of their brain and later being diagnosed with concussion.

Dissection

A dissection session typically lasts from one to three hours. Such sessions often occur in blocks of teaching based around the rest of the medical school curriculum. This might mean that students have one or two dissection sessions each week for a block of eight weeks while they are studying the musculo-skeletal system. Or it could be that they are studying the clinical case of lung cancer and as part of that undertake a dissection session on the lungs and then the following week they move to another clinical case or area of the body. How the medical school curriculum is set out is different at each school but there is an established list (Core Regional Anatomy Syllabus) of what anatomy a medical student needs to know at graduation.

Dissection is the actual art of cutting and exploring the cadaver in a systematic manner. Dissection implies precision, understanding and skill. Dissection always has an aim, for example, it could be to examine the muscles involved in breathing that are in the rib cage or to understand the arrangement of the heart values and how they function. To perform a dissection students need to follow guidelines. Students should be guided, and use their knowledge and their hand to eye coordination. As an example, to understand the muscles involved in breathing students have to skilfully separate out the external intercostal muscle from the internal intercostal muscles beneath. The key part to see is the muscle fibres running in a different direction. This helps the understanding of how the muscles do different jobs. In case you are wondering, the external intercostal muscles help to lift up the rib cage to increase the capacity of the lungs when breathing in. The internal intercostal muscles run the opposite direction and help more with forced expiration when you are blowing air out of the lungs. Quiet expiration is mostly a passive process created by the diaphragm returning to its resting position.

Dissection sessions are often led by one anatomist with a teaching team. For students to undertake dissection they must have had previous related teaching, such as a lecture on the structures being dissected to help them understand what they are looking at. Students also must be guided in dissection by a workbook or manual so that they can neatly move away structures to get to others deeper within the body. If this isn't set up by teachers then students will simply cut through or remove the structure they are looking for.

What is amazing about dissection is the journey it offers into the human body and both teachers and students all feel privileged that donors have allowed that. There are three examples explained below to highlight what actually happens in dissection (Figure 15).

Chest Wall

Examining the front (anterior) of the chest wall and then removing it is a dissection performed often early on in students training. Usually prior to this the students would have removed the pectoralis major and minor muscles that sit just beneath the skin and breast tissue on the chest. They then work to examine the muscles of the chest wall that are involved in breathing - the external and internal intercostal muscles. They run in a beautiful crisscross pattern with the externals running as if your hands are in your front pockets and the internals run as if your hands are in your back pockets creating an 'x' shape. Students dissect a window (a space where you can lift up one muscle to see another one underneath) to see these muscles and their nerve and blood supplies. The clinical relevance to this dissection is that a doctor needs to be able to put a chest drain in. A chest drain is used to remove fluid, air or pus from around the lung, the presence of these can result in the lung(s) collapsing and severely affecting the patient's ability to breath. The doctor needs to know where to place the drain and the muscles the drain goes through.

To lift off the chest wall the students need to start at the sternum (breast bone) and make a cut using a scalpel heading towards the arms. This should be done very carefully because if they cut too deep they will pierce the lungs and damage them. It is also impossible to cut through a rib with a scalpel so when they get to a rib they use the rib sheers. These powerful hand-held shears deserve respect as they can crunch (literally do) through ribs so they could easily crush fingers too (Figure 16). You end up crunching through one rib, then cutting the muscles, all the time being aware of the nerves and vessels; and then another rib and then more muscles and this continues until they have gone all the way around. Once almost free, the chest wall is held in place by just a few ligaments that connect the outer layer around the heart to the inside of the rib cage. These (pericardial sternal) ligaments can be easily broken through with the back of your hand. I really like these ligaments - their job is to help anchor your heart so it doesn't move around. I like the wonderful structure of these ligaments being arranged in many strands, and when being stretched as you lift off the chest they resemble cobwebs, similar to those you would discover lifting up a log. Once the ligaments have been cut students can lift off the thorax. This then shows the arrangement of the heart and lungs as they are undisturbed. It is quite beautiful, like freshly laid snow - you know it will be disturbed and will never look the same again.

The next part of the dissection will be exploration of the heart. The first thing they will notice is the heart is wrapped in a layer that looks like the fat on bacon. This is good, the heart needs this small layer of fat to help insulate it. Hidden in the fat are the very pretty coronary arteries that bring highly oxygenated blood to the heart muscle. I say pretty because they are perfectly forms tubes that sit in a little dip in the fat. These are the arteries that can become blocked and cause a heart attack. One structure that is very clear to see is the aorta that carries oxygenated blood away from the heart to the rest of the body. It is often whiter in colour because it contains elastin fibres to allow it to expand with the output of blood from the heart. A truly amazing fact is that while the aorta is in itself an artery, it also has its own arteries suppling it! A careful look and you can see these as a spider pattern over its surface.

Stomach

The second example is a dissection of the stomach. The stomach, as you may know, is connected to the oesophagus and then the rest of the small intestine. It is actually located on the left side of the body, under the ribs and not central and lower down as many believe. The students would already have dissected the abdominal wall, to show the muscles involved. The rectus abdominus muscle you will know as your *'six pack'*. Students trace this muscle from the xiphoid process at the end of the sternum all the way down to the pubic bone. Everyone has a six pack; some people have theirs more developed than others. It is one long muscle that is separated in the middle by a tendon-like gap called the linea alba (meaning white line). It is also separated in the horizontal plane in places that make it look like a *'six pack'*. Students will also have peeled back the skin covering the external and internal oblique muscles that run at your waist.

The arrangement of these muscles is important in understanding the formation of the inguinal canal where various tubes to the testes pass through. In females a ligament passes through the inguinal canal (round ligament of the uterus). Students have to examine these muscle layers and locate where the entrance and exit point of where the testes had to pass through. This is important clinically, as a hernia develop here in men so students need to know these areas, what they contain and what the nerve and blood supply is. This is also clinically important in diagnosing many other conditions such as an undescended testicle or a twist or injury to the testicle.

Once students have examined the muscles that cover the abdomen and the inguinal canal they move on to explore the organs. Organs within the abdomen are located within a structure called the peritoneum. The peritoneum is a bit like a sac and a lot of the intestines are held within it, held in place by special ligaments. This includes the stomach, and one of the ligament-like structures students will easily identify first is the *'lesser omentum'* that runs from the stomach to the liver. Students will use their hand to feel the extent of the stomach and in feeling upwards will find its junction with the oesophagus. This is a clinical landmark for oesophageal hernia and the area where acid reflux from the stomach can cause problem.

Students will then carefully dissect around the edge of the stomach to locate the arteries that supply it. To undertake this, one student will be making a cut, with another student holding forceps or supporting them, another student will be assisting and showing the other students what they are working on. Once the stomach is a little freer, students can get their hands behind it and feel for the important splenic artery that takes blood to the spleen where old red blood cells are removed. Students can explore the structures that are close to the stomach, the liver, the kidneys and spleen and understand how conditions and surgery of the stomach might affect these other organs. Students then move on to making a cut in the stomach and opening it up to examine the inside structure that is thrown into lots of folds to increase the surface area to facilitate digestion. The final part of the dissection involves students following the stomach into the duodenum (small intestine) and dissecting out surrounding structures to locate where the bile duct (from the liver) and the pancreatic duct (from the pancreas) enters the small intestine. Clinically this is important in cases of gall stones or liver or pancreatic diseases.

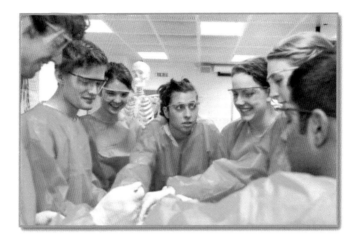

Figure 15. A typical dissection class

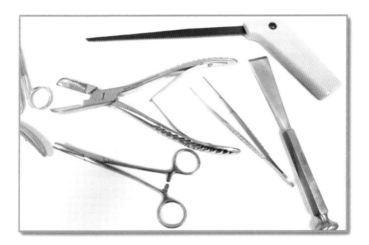

Figure 16. Typical dissection instruments (clockwise from the top; saw, chisel, forceps, rib sheers, artery clamps, scissors (handle only)

Upper Arm

The third example is a dissection of the upper arm and axilla (arm pit). The aim of this dissection is to examine the major arteries and veins that pass to the upper limb and an important nerve network known as the brachial plexus that supplies all of the upper limb. To get into this area of the body students must move the arm so that it is away from the body. This can be easily achieved even on a formalin fixed cadaver by turning the palm to face up and moving the arm. The arm will normally rest away from the body creating a triangle shaped region to work on in the axilla (arm pit). The first part of the dissection here is to remove the skin. This can be quite difficult in the axilla just because of the space confinements. To do this students must use their scalpel and forceps. The forceps hold the skin (instead of using your fingers) and the scalpel must follow a line of where the skin joins to the underlying fat. The next stage is to use scalpels and blunt dissection with scissors (not using the cutting edge but placing the scissors in and then opening them up) to remove the fat and lymph nodes in the axilla. Clinically, understanding the location and function of lymph nodes in the axilla is important in understanding the spread of cancer. The fat in this area can look a white/cream/slightly yellow colour. The lymph nodes also are the same colour so students have to be careful in dissection and look and feel for the change in texture. Fat, as you would expect, is slippery and soft to the touch. Lymph nodes are harder to the touch and can be felt as pea-shaped to grape-shaped.

Slightly deeper to the fat and lymph are the arteries and veins. The main artery, the axillary artery is around 1-2cm in diameter and can be easily cut so students should not go into this area with a scalpel pointing downwards but with the scissors at an angle so they can cut through the surrounding tissue and not into the artery. The artery is easy to palpate, a main artery such as this when fixed feels a lot like squeezing an empty banana skin. Very close to the artery will be the axillary vein. Veins have much thinner walls and feel like squeezing those long tubes of yoghurt used in children's lunchboxes. The artery and veins sit with the network (plexus) of nerves around them. The nerves are also cream/white in colour but can be identified by them being long and slightly flat. Nerves feel more like slightly undercooked noodles.

The main nerves that supply the arm leave the spinal cord in the neck. During development in the embryo they had to mix and join to create a plexus (network). The nerves leave the plexus and travel all the way down to the fingers. To dissect the nerves out from their surrounding connective tissue, students use a scalpel and scissors to gently follow along the nerve freeing it from surrounding tissue. There is a set pattern to these nerves in terms of where they are located and the groups of muscle and area of skin they supply. These nerves are known as the brachial plexus. Understanding this pattern is important in clinical practice in any condition of the upper limb, for example shoulder injuries, broken arms and any repetitive strain injury such as carpel tunnel. Students working on the dissection frequently take it in turns to look at a diagram of this either in the text books, on the iPad or on the board that the anatomy demonstrators have kindly drawn for them (Figure 17).

Only when students have located a nerve they can then remove any surrounding tissue using scissors and can then trace it to see where it goes and so to understand the nerve path. A good example here is your 'funny bone', your humerus bone in your upper arm. You will all know that when you bash your elbow it really hurts! This is because the ulna nerve (one of the nerves of the brachial plexus) runs from within the axilla down and around the outside of the humerus where it forms the elbow close to the surface, so when you bash your elbow you also bash the nerve that is why it hurts so much. In dissection, students must not only look, cut, explore and feel (palpate) with their hands and visually understand with their eyes the anatomical structures, they also should think about the functional significance and how they will be using this information in their medical practice.

The three examples described above show how many different types of skills are required. Some dissections are heavily reliant on scalpels and cutting into structures, for example in the arm. Others such as the stomach are much more about using scissors and blunt dissection. At times, you can dissect a lot with just your hands. Where structures are next to each and are held with connective tissue simply placing your hand in there and gently moving it around will free up a structure and will open the area up for examination.

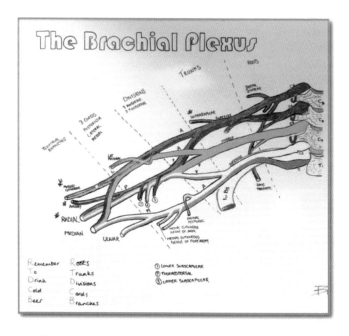

Figure 17. Demonstrator drawing of the brachial plexus

Prosection

Donors can become prosections. These are professional dissections carried out by a Prosector or sometimes junior doctors in training. To do so the body is cut into a region is needed (such as, hip or thorax) and over many hours a prosection is made. To make a prosection a similar process to dissection is undertaken but the aim is different. The aim is not to explore or understand a region (although that very often occurs as a result) but to produce something that shows specific structures that can be used by others to learn from. Prosections are examined and used by a range of students and postgraduate groups to explore the anatomy.

Prosections can offer students a chance to learn a tricky bit of anatomy or reduce the time needed to get into difficult and complex areas like the head. There are some prosections that I can visualise even years later after having used them. There is one of the trigeminal nerve (that is deep in the side of face) that I used at Southampton. The nose and eyes were intact and the prosection went deep into the jaw. It has a very slightly squishy nose where it had been laid facing down at some point. It had the most beautiful dissected branches of the trigeminal nerve that serves your muscles that help you chew food, and also supplies sensation to the face, this is very important clinically. It would have taken twenty plus hours to make this prosection and it was used to teach hundreds of students this difficult area.

A donor who has been used for prosections will have been cut into different parts. Each part labelled so that when it comes to putting the donor back together each and every part is brought together and they are reassembled into a coffin as they would have been. It is part of the HTA regulations that all parts of a donor are tagged and monitored on a system so that it is known where every part is at any one time. Do bits ever get lost I hear you say? The answer is no, although the team might temporarily not be able to locate something. For example, in clearing up a pelvic anatomy class it turned out a pair of testes were missing. They had been out on table 3 with a range of other prosections showing the inguinal canal (groin). The tray system was checked but they were not there. The team were more perplexed than concerned, they knew they wouldn't leave the DR because a) a student would have to be very, very stupid to do this; b) Who would want to, and c) CCTV is in operation in most DRs as a requirement. So, where were they? In the end, it turned out they had been rolled up into the soaking cloths that had been placed over the specimens to keep them wet. They were then put back on the correct shelf.

Pelvis

I am going to use an example here from my time at the University of Southampton. The department only taught using prosections. Each academic term staff had to produce a *'handbook'* that contained a range of exercises and descriptive text on the area to be studied, and I led the reproductive systems course. There were five prosection practicals, each of two hours and divided into six workstations. There were two members of teaching staff in the room and the students could start at any station and were free to move across the DR (Figure 18). Because of student numbers it was necessary to repeat each session three times. The first session was on the pelvic walls, the bony pelvis and the muscles involved. For this session, the six tables would have two-six prosections on them. Some would be duplicates to allow more students to explore the same muscles. Of course, having exact duplicates is not possible so there were two prosections from different donors but made to show the same structures. Other prosections would be created in a slightly different way, or as in the case of the nerves to the pelvis, some nerves would be on one prosection and other nerves on another prosection.

This gave students the opportunity to compare the different anatomy and understand the natural variation that exists.

Students would work in their peer groups. Some would touch the specimens and examine them and follow a nerve or artery and others would observe and learn from fellow students. In the picture below the students are watching a member of staff talk through a few structures via a camera being relayed through the TV screen. You can see the selection of tables with different prosections on (covered up). At BSMS medical students also use prosections. They use them in a similar way to Southampton, especially for areas that are harder to dissect. Prosections are also used for different groups of students and qualified doctors.

Figure 18. A typical prosection class (University of Southampton).

Allied Health Professions

Prosections are also used to teach allied health professional students such as Physiotherapists and Pharmacists. My preference here is to use prosections because such students, when professionals, will be treating patients and based on what their job role entails it is important for them to understand the human form. Physiotherapists are very interested in joint anatomy for example and how the muscles of the limbs and back work. Pharmacists are especially interested in the oral cavity and gastrointestinal system to understand where and how drugs are absorbed. These students get to examine prosections of the stomach and get to see the layers of muscle and the folds of the stomach where certain medications will be absorbed.

Experts

At times surgeons use a specific part of a donor body to undertake specialist training or research. I will explain a couple of examples.

When a group of anaesthetists visits the DR and wish to look at nerve plexuses within the body, they often ask for a selection of upper limbs to show the nerves in the axilla (arm pit). They are very keen on looking at where the nerves branch and how they lay in relation to surrounding structures so that when they inject these nerves they have a better idea of the surrounding anatomy. For this session, they might require me to teach on one table, explaining the detailed anatomy of the wrist and a colleague at another explaining the details of the elbow. This level of teaching is to the highest level. The anaesthetists will have seen this anatomy on a patient, or in a textbook but are looking to us as anatomists to guide them through the anatomy on the prosections. Another table might have a selection of four lower legs, again the nerves have been dissected out on these prosection so that they can trace them as they follow their route into the ankle. Again, they are interested in their landmarks and how in clinical practice they can block these nerves either during surgery or for pain relief.

The anaesthetists also use live ultrasound with a living model (live person) in the DR. This enables them to quickly link the anatomy that they can see in a prosection to the view they see in clinic. As an example, the live ultrasound comes from a portable (laptop) sized device that they can use on the model to find the carpel tunnel (a space in the wrist where many tendons and nerve pass through). After examining the structures on ultrasound, they can then turn to the next table and look at the same structures on a prosection, carefully examining the relationships of the nerves that can become inflamed by pressure from the tendons.

A specialist ear surgery course used ten heads from fixed donors that had been sawn off and then cut into two on the band saw. The surgeons then drill into the temporal bone (at the side of the skull) to practice surgical procedures. The organisers of the course bring in all their surgical instruments, large microscopes, microdissection instrumentation and lavage kits to wash out the canal they are making. The course runs for a couple of days and uses the heads that were used last year by the medical students. The surgeons work with amazing concentration, stopping to discuss progress and the course lead reviews the anatomy and any different approaches that might have been possible. Over a couple of days twenty highly skilled surgeons have had the opportunity to further develop their skills and the surgery they perform. Given that each of the surgeons undertake 500 operations each year the number of patients that benefit from the donation can be into thousands within a couple of years. In the case of very specialist surgery that is only undertaken on a few individuals but the time in the DR experimenting paves the way for future areas that then influences many other surgeries as the practice becomes more common.

Pros and Cons of dissection and prosection

There is debate about whether it is better to teach using dissection or prosection, or both. The debate started in 1957, when the General Medical Council (GMC, the body that regulate medical training and the professional register) said that medical schools could choose not to dissect a whole body. In the end, it comes down to personal preferences and logistics. I believe both methods should be used as they offer slightly different learning experiences. A current review of the evidence has looked at dissection or prosection studies where students examination grades have been compared, showing that neither method is superior. This hence leaves the debate wide open to opinions as to what else other than pure knowledge is gained through either method.

In the case of dissection, I feel it is a journey of discovery. Students physically cut out the layers that cover the heart, seeing the space between them where a small amount of fluid sits to enable the heart to beat in a friction free environment. Students then cut through the major vessels and removing the heart in your hands. This is an experience. You momentarily stop to reflect on how many times the heart has beaten. But once that is done, you rationalise that it's a muscular pump that sucks and pumps blood around. A cool feature is that the heart has its own blood supply - this concept blew my mind when I first heard of it! Arteries take oxygenated blood away from the heart around the body (except for those going to the lungs with deoxygenated blood) and veins carry deoxygenated blood to the heart. Students could learn this from a prosection but when you see these arteries connected as you dissect then you gain an understanding of them. It is also understood that the ability to judge depth (how far away another anatomical structure is) increases with training in anatomy and that three-dimensional understanding of the body is enhanced by the opportunity to explore structures with your hands in dissection.

Dissection offers students the chance to explore pathology and natural variation (how one body differs to another) as they find it. As mentioned, donors with a range of conditions can be accepted. Sometimes students and staff find conditions that were not known to the donor. This opportunity to teach elements of pathology alongside anatomy I feel is very important.

Students using both prosections and dissection can also see natural variation. This is especially enhanced if using prosection where it is possible to have four or five hearts lined up next to each other. Students can not only learn the anatomy but they can through skills of comparison gain an idea that the inside of our bodies does not always match the textbook, and that there is considerable variation in the size of structures and in how branching patterns of arteries can vary.

Others have argued that dissection also offers the student many other skills, including team work, communication and humanity values. I agree with these. When eight students are working around one cadaver, only maybe two or three are cutting at one point in time, another two are assisting with instruments or holding a structure, very much as in surgery. The other students are discussing something with a teacher or working through the notes, or using another resource such as a skeleton.

A downside of dissection is that it is time consuming. There can also be issues within groups. Some students can take over the dissection and others shy away. These are difficult for teachers to manage. It can also be difficult for students to undertake dissections that require a higher amount of skill or a great deal of time to complete. An example could be the muscles that are involved in chewing (mastication). There are four main muscles, with two that can be easily seen after removal of the skin (temporalis and masseter). To get to the remaining two muscles (medial and lateral pterygoids) you saw through the skull just around the temples to remove a piece of bone called the zygomatic arch. Next a piece of the mandible (jaw bone) should be removed with a saw or with bone cutters so that a small area known as the infratemporal fossa (roughly, behind where your jaw joins your skull) can be accessed and it is here that these two muscles are located. They are important - the lateral pterygoid, is the only muscle that acts to pull your jaw downwards as in opening the mouth. It is helpful to understand these muscles in many conditions such as lock jaw, stroke or trauma. As you can imagine a dissection like this would take many hours so a pre-prepared prosection is ideal. The prosector has spent this time and from here many medical students can view and examine this prosection and understand the muscles without having to spend the hours undertaking it themselves.

During my PhD work, I investigated a donor in 1970, who had given consent for retention of body parts. A prosection showing some very intricate nerves and arteries of the pelvis had been saved. The prosection was used for over 30 years, and I estimate that over 4,000 medical students have had the chance to learn from it.

There are some areas where dissection does not suit everyone. Personally, I do not like dissecting feet very much, they are often dry and difficult to do. I think it's the texture I don't like. Once some fresh frozen feet had been shipped in from the United States and they looked so much like the chicken in my lunch that it put me off chicken for a couple of weeks. On the other hand I do like an exploration into an abdomen; it's very satisfying. I have to stand up tall, or be on tip toes, especially if the abdomen is a little rotund, check your sleeve coverage and that there are no gaps between your gloves and your gown and get your hands in. It's a lovely cavity to explore, many spaces and again lots to find out. Some people have adhesions which is a bit like scar tissue and it causes organs to 'stick' to each other. The size of an individual's stomach is always fascinating, some people have large stomachs and I can only postulate that they ate a large amount on a regular basis. Some donors stomachs are just as wide as the rest of their intestine. The stomach is after all a dilated portion of the gut tube, its only claim to fame is that it has an extra layer of muscle to help it 'churn' food. I say 'churn' as food does move around, but it was discovered by Army surgeon William Beaumont (1785-1835) that digestion is a result of chemicals rather than mechanical movements. How did he find this out? Genius! He used an individual who had a gunshot wound to his stomach and put bits of food on a metal wire into the stomach. He noted that the food was dissolved by the contents of the stomach i.e. the acid.

The stomach's next door neighbour, the duodenum, is very clever. It knows if the acid levels of the food entering it (now called 'chyme') are going to be very high in acid, so high that it could cause chemical burns. It needs to protect itself from the acid so it has special glands called Bruner's glands and these secrete a very alkaline substance to help protect the wall of the duodenum. The duodenum then goes into the jejunum and ileum before passing to the large intestine. Another reason to like the abdomen, good names!

There is sometimes not a divide between a medical school using dissection or prosection and this is called a hybrid approach. A practical class can incorporate both methods - students can work on donors using dissection but for certain structures students can walk over and examine the prosections, or students have separate dissection and prosection classes based on the area being studied.

Fresh frozen

When donors are preserved as 'Fresh Frozen' the body is frozen whole or taken into parts and frozen as parts. This is very useful for surgical training where surgeons, anaesthetists and A&E doctors, et cetera, work through new procedures on the cadaver. This part of training is invaluable in reducing surgical errors and allowing for the development of new surgical techniques. Not all medical schools in the United Kingdom undertake this and at times it is necessary for fresh frozen material to be imported from overseas. Three examples of how fresh frozen is used follows.

Foot Surgery
An international company that supplies the surgical field with specialist equipment often needed for foot and sometimes lower leg surgery needed to prove their equipment and train surgeons in how to use it. The equipment is a complex metal and plastic system that is used in a range of surgeries such as bunion repair through to complex rebuilding of ankles. This type of surgery changes people's lives and often enables individuals to walk again. The company brings all their equipment in and arranges a course for surgeons to practice. The surgeons spend many hours undertaking the surgery using the equipment. They prefer to use fresh frozen and will order the feet themselves directly with a company in the United States. When the feet arrive at London Gatwick Airport they are transferred to us and once on our premises are cared for under our licence.

Ear Nose and Throat Surgery
Another group of consultants training in maxillofacial surgery (maxillofacial surgeons need to qualify in both medicine and dentistry) had requested 10 fresh frozen heads. The heads arrive frozen and were then defrosted. The surgeons work on them over an intense day, undertaking a range of surgical procedures, documenting minute detail such as the direction of stiches and the small arteries they have used.

The procedures mimic surgeries such as removing tumours of the face, a cleft palate repair or the removal of impacted wisdom teeth. In one surgery the surgeons are working out how to remove a possible tumour on the face of a patient back in the hospital. They have marked out where the tumour extends to and carefully cut around the delicate nerves in that area as if they were operating to remove the tumour. The surgeon concerned did the operation for real on the patient just two days later and it was a success.

Once the course has finished and the team have cleaned up the DR, the heads are moved into the prep room. It is a time like this when my brain does struggle to compute what it sees. It can see 10 heads lined up on a table, some have blood dripping from them, some have stiches from surgery across the nose and cheek. It's a mental image that will never leave me, not because I find it disgusting or shocking, but because in our human lives individuals are not expected or conditioned to see this type of thing, it goes against what humans are trained to find acceptable.

Burns Reconstruction Surgery

A group of plastic surgeons (Figure 19) wanted to practice how to reconnect blood vessels. The surgery they wished to practice is an intricate process where a muscle flap is lifted from one area to then be reattached to cover another area. A key part is the blood supply. It is possible to dissect out very tiny blood vessels and to then reattach them. To check if the reattachment would have been good quality, blue food dye is pushed through the vessel so you can easily see how far it flows, and to understand if the operation would have been viable in a patient. It is through practice like this that surgeons become more expert. This example also hopefully shows you how they can try a new idea or test out a different method of re-connecting a vessel that they have a reasonable idea might work. Of course they could not try this out on a patient without good evidence that it will be better or equivalent to established practice. Following this session, a national course was established to aid with joining arteries back to arteries when an area of skin or muscle has been moved as part of surgery.

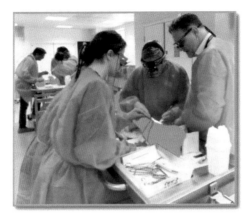

Figure 19. A surgical course using the DR (leg has been blocked out so no detail is shown)

Simulation

It is possible to get quite creative with simulation. To assist in training on how to remove a lump, or a cyst filled with puss we can make a simulation by placing a square of skin over a board. Then between the board the finger part of a glove filled with custard (good cheap custard) is placed. The finger part of the custard glove can be attached to the board to simulation connective tissue. When the skin is placed on top and the area covered in a surgical drape it looks and feels very real (Figure 20). A cherry tomato can be placed in the same way but this time to simulate a fine needle biopsy, perhaps being taken to remove cells that are thought to be cancerous.

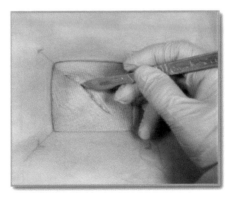

Figure 20. Mock set up for a cyst removal

Research into anatomy

You might be thinking that by now there was sufficient detailed knowledge of the body's anatomy that there is nothing further to investigate through research. However, there are many components of anatomy that science is still exploring and discoveries are shared through academic journals such as *'Clinical Anatomy'*. One of these areas is natural variation.

Variations in anatomy from person to person are common and yes, each of us has a heart but the order in that main vessels leave the main artery (aorta) can vary. I have drawn the text book standard below (Figure 21) but then also drawn out the two most common variants. You can see that the first variation affects around 15% of the population. It is likely that a doctor will encounter this in a patient. Therefore, dissection or prosection is so important to see the reality that the body often does not follow the textbook norm. Our body is full of these amazing variations. Another good example that you can see on yourself is a muscle in our lower arm that goes into the palm of our hand, called palmaris longus. This muscle is only present in some of the population. The absence of palmaris longus varies from 2% to 64% in different populations across the world. It is an evolutionary hangover from when our ancestor species used to climb trees because it is a weak flexor, it also helps tense the palm. To test if you have it, look for a central tendon in your wrist when you flex your wrist against resistance (Figure 22).

Research in anatomy aims to determine the frequency and details of such variation. As an example, a muscle that is not often present is the sternalis, located just behind the sternum (breast bone). Research has shown it to be present in 1%-18% of the population depending on the world location. Doctors were interested in this muscle, how often it is found in donor bodies and the different shapes and sizes of this muscle. The variation in this muscle matters to doctors who are treating patients in areas such as breast surgery and radiology.

Other examples of research in anatomy are about clinical procedures and how the anatomy is related to a specific procedure. My first study in this area explored the relationship of the femur to bone cement that is used in hip replacement surgery. I have also supervised surgeons and medical students who wanted to test the strength and best way of suturing (stitching) tendons back together if they had been severed through injury of the hand. The study involved cutting tendons in a donor's hand and then using different techniques to re-join the tendons and evaluate each one. Research in anatomy is very varied and is often based around an everyday clinical need.

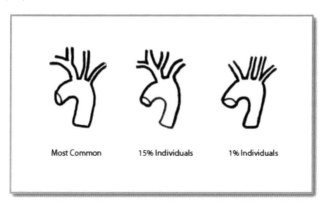

Figure 21. Common variants of the aortic arch

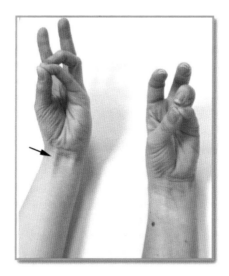

Figure 22. How to determine if you have a palmaris longus muscle. It is present in the individual on the left marked by the arrow. It is absent in the individual on the right (me).

Chapter 5. The end of the donation

The time when donors are *'finished with'* varies greatly, it is influenced by the teaching need. It can be as short as three months or up to three years. This unknown time frame can be very difficult for families especially if they choose to be notified when that time comes. Some families may say after six months that this is too soon, they are not ready, or some families wait each day for the phone call that their loved one's body will be returned to them, which could be years.

Notification

At the end of the donor's time there is an important process that takes the body from being a *'cadaver with a number'* back to being a *'named donor'*. The medical school decide as to when they have finished with a donor. This is to either due to the time constraint (three years) as given in the consent or it because the anatomy department has simply finished doing as much as they can with the donor. Where the consent requires the body to be returned within three years, anatomists are mindful not to make it too close to this.

For my region, once the decision is made to release the donor back to the next of kin the London Anatomy Office inform the family if they requested this at the time of donation. The London Anatomy Office gives the family one month notice of when the cremation (or burial - but this is rare) will be. Families then have a choice as to whether they wish to be informed at the time of the cremation, attend the cremation, take possession of the ashes and attend the memorial service. Some choose to attend all, others just the funeral and cremation. Approximately 60% of families attend the funeral and cremation, which has increased over the years, it used to be around 10% several years ago. This represents the increase in donors we take with terminal conditions (for example cancer) as those donors are more likely to have living family that can attend the cremation and memorial service.

Coffins

Coffins are a kind of final wrapping for your body. Just the shape of a coffin is iconic. Over the years, I have seen hundreds of coffins. Priests and funeral home providers have seen many more. There is an age-old riddle of the coffin that goes something like *'The individual who makes it doesn't need it. The individual who buys it doesn't need it and the individual who uses it never knows about it.- what is it?'*

Once it has been decided to release a donor from our care I have the responsibility to place them in their coffin. The department is provided with standard sized and grade coffins. The donor is carefully and respectfully placed in their coffin. As you can imagine they might be quite heavy and it takes Lydia, Lucinda, myself and another member of the team to take the donor from the table or body store and carefully lower them into the coffin. The donor documents are all checked by myself and then double checked by another person designated on the site HTA licence.

Where additional consent is in place for parts of the donor to be retained beyond three years, an arm for example, the rest of the donor's body is placed in the coffin and the arm is placed on a table next to the coffin so that I can clearly see it and check the label and documentation. All donor numbers and tags on body parts are checked, recorded and documented. The coffins I will always remember are those where the head is retained. It is just like any other body part in terms of being made of bone, muscles, nerves et cetera, but a coffin containing a body with no head just affects my mind more than anything.

Inside the coffin, I place a cardboard support under the head. Any material taken out of the body during dissection or prosection (every single bit of material taken out) is added back in. I place this material in a sealed bag between the feet. Any donors that have been cut up are always reassembled. I could put it in all mixed up, no one would know, but I wouldn't, it's part of humanity, respect is central and very important. Hence if the prosector had cut the right arm off or taken the liver out, these would be placed back in their correct position.

One thing that does affect the placing of donors in coffins is their height. With individuals of short stature this is not too much of a problem but tall individuals can cause a problem. In general, they are okay for our tables but too tall for the coffins. After one episode, the technician always now measures donors and orders different sizes of coffins. But on this occasion when putting a donor in a standard coffin it was clear that they were too tall. The Prosector at the time worked out a few different options. First, they tried to slide the body in, pulling them down so their head is in and feet are in. This didn't work. Second, they tried to create a bend at the knees to see if that worked. No luck. Bending the knees means it was not possible to get the coffin lid on. The only option left was to break the legs. The Prosector used a saw to make a cut into the bone, but not all the way through so that the leg was detached. The leg was then raised and with the force of two people the leg was broken but remained attached. This way it was possible to keep the legs attached but they had been turned facing the wrong way. At the time of doing this I was guided by a Prosector who had been in the role for a long time. It felt so incorrect. I do regret it. It went around in my head like a movie on replay. It was not the way I would want to treat an individual, but here was not much choice. It would have been very difficult and a heavy lift for us to remove the individual from the coffin and while waiting for a replacement coffin the body would have started to decay, this seemed equally disrespectful. To remove the head seemed a worse alternative. But even as I think again about this, I want to say sorry again to the individual.

The other difficulty is if the donor has been slightly too rotund for the coffin. This was easier to deal with and it took the funeral services and three of us holding the coffin lid shut to enable the screws to be done up.

In all cases, once all checks and paperwork are complete I screw down the coffin lid and the coffin is taken away for cremation or burial.

At BSMS, for logistical reasons we try and arrange an exit of coffins undertaken over a couple of days once a year. This reflects the cycle of teaching. Teaching has finished, many courses have run for experts, and this time enables us to get ready for the next cycle and the new academic year. We do put donors in their coffins at other times too but this is when most of it occurs. During this time everyone in the anatomy team helps and in pairs we work though one donor and coffin at a time. At the end of one day I had signed 23 cremation forms. The funeral services can only take four coffins at a time so it is over the following days that the funeral team collected these. There are a few logistical things here to explain. I ordered 23 empty coffins. Space around the medical school is limited, fought over and jealously guarded. I am crafty, and slowly as the funeral services dropped the empty coffins off in batches of four, I stashed them around the building. I managed to get four hidden in the Audio-Visual room at the front of the lecture theatre, literally behind the lecture theatre main screen. I managed to get another ten in a teaching room that does not belong to the medical school and that I suspected no one was using (well if they were they didn't complain!) I put a few by the back stairs and the rest in the preparation room. Simple! I then had to ask anyone who was around the building that day not to come in to the DR and help, but to help carry empty coffins from wherever I had stashed them round to the DR door.

Completing this procedure makes for a few really tiring days. Most donors will still be as a largely complete body and carefully they are rolled from the table directly into a coffin with four people helping. This is messy, there is often some preserving fluid that leaks out or has pooled on the tables and splashes you as you move the body. Once one member of the anatomy team has checked the contents of the coffin, and another member of the team has double checked, the coffin can be sealed and then it needs to be lifted to the side of the room for storage. This continues until all the donors who happened to be on the top level of the tables has been completed. Now unlike the pristine tables at the start of term when the team put these donors on, getting the higher-level donor off would have created dripping and spillage of fluid so the table might need to be cleaned up a bit before the team can place sandbags on the top and very carefully rotate the tables, to get the lower level donor back on top. This is hard and takes four people to do a controlled lift, otherwise it will swing and could potentially tip over. The DR continues to look a mess as space becomes short. Tables are cleared of donors and coffins in groups of four are laid out, ready for the funeral services. Each coffin has a *'coffin card'* attached and the documentation is all together. Signing for several coffins to be removed for cremation is a responsibility I take very seriously and I always say thank you in my head to the individual as the coffin is closed. They are the most amazing silent teachers.

Cremation

Once the coffins have been collected from us they are taken to the funeral home. On arrival at the funeral home an engraved plate with the donor details is screwed onto the coffin. When the time for the service and cremation comes (this can be a few days depending on the logistics) the donor is driven to the crematorium in a hearse (at other times donor bodies are transported in private ambulances). In London they are then carried by Dignity Funerals, where Martin Drew is a Funeral Director.

The funeral team is led by Martin in a standard procession into the crematorium where a short service occurs. If there are no relatives present the funeral takes place with the Chaplain and the funeral team at the crematorium. I have sat in on some of these funerals. They are a very dignified short service. If family or friends are present then Martin and his team adapt to their need. The chaplain contacts the family/next of kin a week prior to the cremation to discuss the service and ask if they would like to have something shared. It is also possible for them to accommodate other faiths. The family might wish to place flowers or a photograph on the coffin, or choose a certain piece of music, or say a few words. After the service the family is taken to the London Anatomy Office Garden of Remembrance memorial plaque and any flowers can be placed here (Figure 23). The Chaplains who preside over this role are part of the University or Hospital Trusts associated with the medical schools and undertake these events in rotation, so it is not possible to ensure that donors at BSMS are cremated at the service where the BSMS chaplain is undertaking this.

After the coffin is committed it is passed through a hatch while the curtains are still drawn. Staff at the crematorium check for a final time the details of the individual but the coffin is never opened once closed by the medical school. The cremator can only cremate one body at a time. It takes about an hour for each body. Therefore each coffin may be stored for a an hour before the staff at the crematorium can place the coffin in a cremator. At the end of the cremation are the remnants of bones that are collected and reduced into finer ashes. If the family are collecting the ashes they are placed into an urn. If the ashes are not to be collected they are scattered at the garden of remembrance.

Figure 23. The London Anatomy plaque at the garden of remembrance.

Very occasionally the individual requests a burial rather than cremation after the medical school has finished with their donated body. This can be difficult at some burial grounds due to the type of embalming that has occurred. When a burial occurs, it is the same process up to the point where the medical school funeral directors will take the coffin back to their funeral home, but then the families' funeral director collects them for burial. It is up to the family to arrange the funeral and cover the associated expenses.

I have mentioned that with the appropriate consent it is possible to keep part of a donor for longer than three years. With the rest of the body having been cremated there is then the question of how we dispose of the remaining parts. The options for this are limited. Twenty years ago, it was possible to undertake a cremation of a coffin that contained a mixture of such body parts from different donors. Cremation regulations changed and the most common route then became clinical incineration.

Clinical incineration occurs for a wide range of items, such as organs removed during surgery, and limb amputations. To undertake this the organ (for example a liver) is placed in a suitable container (a specially designed yellow and red box that also gets incinerated) that becomes sealed when the lid is placed on. The box is then placed in the main yellow clinical waste bin just before the truck collects it. The driver signs to say they have collected a yellow bin containing human material. The lorry then goes east to Kent where all the other yellow waster bins collected on the lorry are dealt with. Since our bin contains human material it then goes west all the way to Southampton.

I was fine with this option until the time when I took a duty of care visit to an incinerator. We have a legal responsibility to ensure we dispose of controlled waste appropriately and because this is contracted out we visit the company to ensure they are undertaking this responsibility on our behalf. I collected Lucinda from Southampton train station and went to a large industrial area on the edge of the New Forest.

Once the yellow bin containing waste from BSMS has reached the incinerator, the waste bin goes on a lift and is opened into the rotating incinerator. The empty bin is brought back down. Only one to two percent of the contents of the mass incinerator are of such a sensitive nature. The rest is other waste or burn off fuel from the local refinery. None of this is against regulation or is of any cause for concern but I felt it was not the dignified end that one might have expected for their liver or heart et cetera, so I started to find out how I could change it.

I discovered that after major incidents (terrorist attacks, plane crashes) where parts of bodies remain but cannot be identified, they are cremated together in a coffin. This would not be suitable for anatomy, where we know who the body parts belong to, but it started a dialogue to see if cremation rather than clinical incineration could be an option. I worked with coroners, Human Tissue Authority, funeral services and crematorium managers to gain support and a way forward to be able to cremate individual parts. The ashes (if any, ashes are mainly bone so an organ such as a liver would not produce any ashes, it will just burn into nothing) will be placed at the plot in the garden of remembrance (South London Crematorium). I am pleased that this will mean that clinical incineration of body parts will reduce over time and become a thing of the past as cremation becomes the preferred option.

Memorial Service

Most medical schools have a memorial service to thank their donors. This is not the funeral but a service that occurs once a year to acknowledge the gift of donation. Some medical schools invite the relatives of donors, others do not. The first such service I attended was in Bristol in 1999 as they opened their new DR and it was held in the DR itself. It was a quick service and felt like a good time to acknowledge this truly amazing gift, but there were no families present.

University of Southampton

As I engaged more in the anatomical community I learnt more about what other medical schools did and realised that at Southampton this was an important event that was missing. I suggested we hold an annual service to my boss and the team were all on board apart from one person who was adamant they did not want to go. At the time, I thought they were just being rude or selfish, but now with experience I can understand a little more. It was about self-preservation, as everyone involved in anatomy must deal with how they feel about the donors and what they do with them in their own personal way. For our first ever service, the students were great and came together with readings and pieces of music to play. It was hosted in the university concert hall and around forty relatives of donors attended.

One couple arrived about an hour early and, in struggling how best to entertain them, I asked a colleague (Dr. Scott Border) to take them for a cup of tea. I didn't realise at the time but it was very difficult for him as he had to discuss their loved one and the work he did. They were very grateful but I am sorry Scott! After the service, there were cakes and tea and the staff and students mixed with the relatives. I am normally fine at striking up general conversation but here I found my eyes drawn to the faces of the families more than at any normal event. I knew what my brain was trying to do. It was trying to place faces of relatives to those who I had been working on. Scott and I taught together on head and neck anatomy for several years so we both had an almost photographic memory of the head specimens. I can close my eyes now and almost scroll through thirty plus prosections that I know well, even years after leaving Southampton I can still see them in my mind. At that memorial service I recognised two faces of relatives that I could connect to a donor. Strangely, once my brain had done that, that was it, no further mental processing was required.

London

Every year the London Anatomy Office hosts a large memorial service for all that year's donors. This is a very special event. At the time of death and the donor being accepted the family are asked if they wish to be informed of when this service will occur. The service takes place in the spring at a large venue in London, and has been previously at Southwark Cathedral (Figure 24). It is hosted in turn by one of the London and South East Medical schools each year. In 2018, it was BSMS's turn to host. The hosts are responsible for organising the event, the speakers, music and provide students as ushers. The service itself lasts around an hour. However, families often gather a good 40 minutes before the service to meet with each other and to get a seat. Over recent years despite the capacity of over a thousand, these events have been standing room only. A mixture of individuals attend the service; families who have had the body of a loved one returned that year, students from the host institution and staff who work in anatomy. At the start of the service the academic faculty and Martin and his team process through the venue to take their seats. Several readings are given and a few hymns sung.

Overleaf is a poem that was written by a Second-Year Medical Student at BSMS for the 2018 service.

Confessions of A Second Year By Katie Clifford

I did not want to meet you
I feared the day our paths would cross.
Not because of blood, or nausea-
But because I knew what it meant.
Your heart had ceased.
Your soul departed.
Departed!?
Where had you gone? What had you seen? How did it feel?
And, more importantly- who had you left behind?

These were all the questions I had, the very first time we met.
Although, even if I could have asked you- I wouldn't have
Because you were a stranger-
And that would be rude!

So, for the next few weeks I tried to stick to small talk.
Focus on the science.
Cling to the dissection notes.

I marvelled at the complexity of your body
Traced the networks of arteries and veins and capillaries and nerves and nodes
and fibres and….
And..
Then it hit me!
I knew more about your insides than I did my own.
And yet- I didn't know what made you tick.
I didn't know what made you happy, or sad, or angry, or mad.
I didn't know the last time you cried,
Or the last movie you watched.
I didn't know the people you loved,
Or the lives you'd changed.

But… I knew my life was different.
This was more than science, or anatomy, or academia. This was about life.
And death.
And giving.
And selflessness.
You believed in something greater.
And for that - I truly thank you

P.S. I no longer fear meeting you.

In fact… I kind of look forward to it.

I never have a dry eye throughout the service. I only have to look around at the thousand plus relatives to think that each of them lost someone very dear to them. On top of their grief they had to deal with the logistics of their loved one donating their body. Several phone calls; the fact they might not have had a funeral; the call, up to three years later, to say their loved one's body was ready to be returned. I feel for each relative. They often bring pictures of their loved one and these are placed on tables at the front. After the service is over and the academic facility and religious representatives have processed out, I turn straight around and go to look at the pictures and to talk to the relatives. I don't find this easy, but this is nothing compared to their pain and loss and I feel it is important that we are there so they can ask us any questions.

Many families then go off for lunch together and the anatomists do the same. It is an emotional day and again the sense of community within anatomy is there. Our lunch discussions are light and friendly, but such times also make us think of our own losses. As my kind colleague Professor Ceri Davies said to me at the first memorial service since losing my own father, *'deep breath and what would you like to drink?'*

Brighton and Sussex Medical School

As staff we always attend the London service described above. For students, who cannot go every year a memorial service is held in the DR just for them. This is very much like the one I first attended in Bristol. I have been working with the University to develop this and to also get a memorial tree and a circular bench sited in the grounds near to the medical school as a permanent reminder. I was also very struck when I joined BSMS that in addition to their usual opening lectures about their course, the students received a talk from a relative whose father had donated his body. I have sat and listened to this talk several times and it always makes a tear appear. I think the talk brings it home for students and highlights to them the impact the gift of donation has on the family that they leave behind.

Donating your body affects the normal process of others being able to physically see a coffin being buried or cremated a week or so after the death. It also means that after this there is no set location at that time to visit, to be close to a loved one. I am completely in awe of the person who visits each year to tell our new students this, they are very lucky to gain such a personalised view.

Figure 24. Southwark Cathedral at the 2017 Memorial Service.

Chapter 6. Working in a Dissecting Room

I am going to explain more on the environment that anatomists work to perform their duties of anatomical examination. Within the DR there are very strict health and safety regulations. If you hate health and safety, a dissecting room would not be for you. I have around 40 standard operating procedures (SOPs) and just as many risk assessments. Now you might be thinking this must be an unsafe place to work! Well of course there are risks.

There is often *'body juice'* and fatty deposits that makes the floor slippery and moving around potentially hazardous. No matter how clean and how often the floor is cleaned, this happens. It is also a place where scalpels, forceps, saws, et cetera. are used, so accidents can happen.

Injuries

More dangerous machinery like the larger band saws have safety guards and operating procedures so thankfully major accidents are very rare. A more common injury risk is due to moving the bodies of donors - they are heavy… seriously, they are a dead weight (pardon the pun). They weigh more dead than alive because of all the embalming fluid. If even a part of a specimen rolls or moves it can cause injury.

A roll call of my own injuries (all minor) will give you an idea:

- I have slipped and fallen, due to fat on the floor, but not injured myself.
- I have cut my fingers and hands on ribs.
- I have crushed my thumb when dropping a head and neck on a table. I had lifted the head up to examine it and move it slightly but it was slippery and fell with my thumb underneath it. It hurt and brought tears to my eyes. Nothing more than a good bruise though.
- I have given myself repetitive strain injury from dissecting and using forceps between my thumb and first finger.
- I have also caught the side of my hand when a body lift dropped slightly, again nothing more than a bruise.

Yes, these are all minor but major things do and can happen. These are not the only injuries that can occur in the DR.

Minor cuts occur fairly often as this is a risk associated with working with sharp objects. Usually just a plaster is fine. However, it is not just the sharp instruments that can cause cuts. There are some areas of a cadaver itself that are very sharp. When a dissection has occurred and the ribs have been cut through they tend not to leave clean edges, instead the ribs leave sharp pieces of bone still protruding. When you go to feel around the outside edge of the lungs to get the lungs ready to be removed, the backs of your hands get scraped by the rib shards. This can be just enough to break a glove but frequently it results in open cuts to the back of your hands. When a cut occurs, it is important to wash it thoroughly to remove any traces of human material and any trace of chemicals.

More major cuts can occur. A colleague (Lucinda) did manage to put a knife through her little finger while dissecting. The knife cut through a tendon called flexor digiti minimi. At the time, she knew it was not a minor cut and phoned the emergency number and went to Accident & Emergency at the local hospital. Surgeons repaired the tendon but then it ruptured, got infected and following three operations Lucinda still has one more surgery to go through to graft a tendon from her leg into her hand to hopefully enable her finger to regain full function. Of course, management ask if there is anything that could have / should have been done. The answer is no, if you work with sharp implements in any form, (chefs, builders, et cetera.) you know and understand the tools of your trade. Lucinda is highly conscientious and very good with health and safety. Neither Lucinda or the institution could have done anything different.

Chemicals

Within a DR there are also some pretty nasty chemicals. There are many procedures and measures in place to manage these. Predominantly formaldehyde, phenol, industrial methylated spirit and alcohol are stored in fire proof cabinets and are all used to assist with the preservation of donors. On one occasion, I had just got home having returned from another site and my phone rang. It was Lydia phoning to say that the university emergency response number had been dialled as one of the team had accidentally spilt some phenol on their leg and had sustained a chemical burn. The university response team came over and advised them to wash it in the shower under running water for 20 minutes. They then went to Accident & Emergency where they were monitored for several hours, but thankfully this healed well.

But what were they doing? Well in this case just getting out some industrial methylated spirits that are used on certain brains that are being created into expert prosections. They opened the chemical cupboard and the bottle of phenol rolled out and cracked. They lifted it up to place it in a safe container unaware that the bottle had split. In the panic of the moment they also then poured some phenol on the brain rather than the chemical they were supposed to. The priority was the member of staff and once it had been established they were okay the attention turned to making the DR safe. I cancelled a practical class for the morning and very quickly and helpfully the University Health and Safety manager was involved. Because there had been a chemical spill the DR was closed and we were not permitted to enter unless wearing protective masks. One subsequent problem was our protective masks are stored in the DR. This was eventually resolved with suitable masks being located from a science laboratory in a nearby building. Myself, the Prosector and my deputy went in, checked everything was OK, and disposed of the brain and the split chemical bottle. The place got a full clean down (Figure 25) and after the air handling system had run for an hour to undertake ten air changes, the DR was back open. Of course, following up on the root cause of this, it has been considered as to why that bottle could have rolled out in the first place and this has since been addressed.

Figure 25. Dr. Smith (left), Dr. Dilley (centre) and Ms. Carline (right) with masks getting ready to clear up the Phenol spillage.

Mould

One thing that is a constant headache for most DRs is mould. This can occur on both tissue that is fixed and unfixed. You might not expect embalmed tissue to go mouldy, but sometimes it does. It might be from a small spore that was already on the donor or it might be from a student or a member of staff sneezing and passing it on. In most cases, a few spots of mould are easy to deal with, either it can be removed or soaked away. My technicians spend a lot of time and effort to check specimens for mould. Sometimes though it can spread and there is little that can be done, except to dispose of the prosection, if it is on a body part. If the mould is on a full body this is slightly harder.

On one occasion one of the heads had a small amount of mould. Mould if left unchecked can spread and can make the whole body unsuitable to be studied. The technician removed the mould and covered the head in cloths soaked in chemicals that usually get rid of it, but it didn't work. Despite our best efforts nothing would shift the mould. There were two options, either to remove the head and place it in the black box until the time it went into its coffin, or to wrap it, seal it and never undo it. As teaching was nearly over and it was only a month until a time when the cadaver would be placed in a coffin I decided on the latter option. The technician wrapped the head in cloths and then in plastic and taped the plastic down. Infection control measures were put in place so gloves were always removed after that donor had been touched. This might seem a little strange but if normally if I touch a donor or if I use a prosection, unless there was donor material stuck on the glove I would not necessarily change them every time. Some practical sessions I might get through four pairs of gloves, others twenty four.

Mould is also a health and safety concern and when it is spotted it is treated as a priority. To protect us when treating a body with mould, face masks are worn as extra protection. Our face masks are all fitted to our own faces and they are tested to ensure there is no leakage when we move around. Face mask testing is quite fun as Catherine shows (Figure 26).

Figure 26. Face mask testing (Catherine Hennessy)

Other things that can go wrong

There was one day several years ago when a series of events occurred. I will explain these in more detail.

Unexpected 1: Blood down the drain
I walked in to the preparation area for the laboratory to see a suction bucket of blood and bone drillings, et cetera, being poured down the drain – not what I would expect as normal practice! On asking I discovered it was from the 20 fresh heads. They did it because it has always been done that way. I knew though that this practice was outdated and I had to ensure that this practice stopped there. I instructed that in future granules were added to any liquid matter and disposed via clinical waste properly rather than washed down the drain.

Unexpected 2: Body missing paperwork.
A donor had been received. The identity of the donor was known, they had a coffin card (that contains key details such as their name, date of birth and death and their unique number) but the rest of the documentation was missing. Our standard operating procedure is to not do anything until this arrives, however this leaves us with a dilemma. What if the documents were never received? What would happen if the documents were on their way but they did not arrive before teaching starts? The teaching sessions would be one cadaver short. This has happened a couple of times before but had always been quickly resolved.

In this case, the set of documents had been missing for many months. The office had chased many times. They were sitting with the next of kin to complete. I can understand that at such a stressful and disorientating time (I have been through this with my father) that it is easy to not do everything you need to. On the other hand, the office were reminding the family frequently. Maybe for the family completing these last forms made it feel real or final, or maybe they did not agree with the donation. It got to the point on this day that a set number of months had passed and I started to gather what I needed for the process for having to give the body back to the family untouched. As I was doing this I received an email with the missing documents and this meant that anatomical examination could begin.

Unexpected 3: Lone worker alarms - why bother?
Lone worker alarms are in place so that if you are the only person in the DR and you fall or slip then an alarm will be activated. These are small credit card like devices that you clip onto your scrubs. If they are held at an angle for a certain amount of time, such as if you have passed out on the floor, they are triggered. If triggered, the first call is to the phone in the DR, in case you have simply left the alarm on your scrubs when getting changed or are just having a snooze! If the DR phone is not picked up, then another phone in the medical school building is called so that someone can come and check on you. If no one answers this phone, the on-call phone is called at the same time as university security who have an emergency access card and can come and rescue you.

So despite the system being all set up for over a year I was about to discover that a former employee had purposefully decided they did not need to use this system. The Medical School Dean's secretary was wondering what to do if they got called to check on someone wearing the alarm. It turned out to be a bit of a tangle. The Deans office couldn't do anything about it, if it did get the call because they don't have access to the DR. Then the main individual who should be wearing the lone worker alarm said it was a moot point because they don't wear it anyway, they felt that they work safely and it's a pain to wear! I struggled to understand this mindset. There is a procedure and system in place to protect your life, why would you not use it? I guess this is like those who do not wear seat belts or cycle helmets. The evidence is there but they choose otherwise. In this case, it is not their choice, it is a health and safety requirement so they had to wear it or be removed from duty. Most anatomists at some point have slipped, fallen, or had some injury in the DR so it is important that health and safety is taken seriously.

Things that just turn up at anatomy laboratories

One of the things that occurs is that members of the public find things in all sorts of places. The types of items that are found are things like a kidney in a jar or a skeleton. They don't know what to do with it and somewhere along the line a medical school is suggested as somewhere that could be interested.

Skeletons in closets

For various reasons members of the public have got in touch to say they have a skeleton they wish to donate. Some of these are historical from the days when every medical student was given or bought a skeleton of their own to learn from. It was around the year 2000 that from this route I acquired my own skeleton (not my own, obviously, but another I could use for study and teaching). A London medical school was closing a campus and they had a considerable number of anatomical skeletons to dispose of. A colleague who worked there at the time sold it to me for £80. A couple of years later another colleague was getting rid of a high quality wooden skeleton box and so I moved the skeleton into it. This is a male skeleton, is easily over 100 years old and is believed to be of Indian origin. India was thought to be the world's supplier of medical bones. Despite the trade being banned in 1985, there is still evidence it goes on. It is thought that many skeletons were acquired by grave robbing. Some of the skeletons that have been donated are from families with some medical background who say these belonged to their great grandfather, then their father and that they have been in the loft since! Others might come from sources that used them for education but no longer wish to have them, such as schools or hospitals.

When a bone or a whole skeleton is donated the first thing is to establish that nothing untoward has occurred, i.e. it had not just been dug up. Skeletons created for anatomy education are often wired together or have a company's markings on them. Some bones are labelled with small numbers that correspond to an identity list, so it is easy to work out that the tibia (lower leg bone) belongs to a set. Other bones have been painted to show where certain muscles attach. If there are any concerns this would be raised to the HTA. I have not had any instances where we have been unable to verify that the bones are not 'medical' and have been intended for anatomy education.

The bones are examined and if they are in a state that is still useable they are added to our ever-growing collection. The details of the bones are recorded under our licence and assigned an identity number. BSMS holds a collection of over a thousand bones. All of these have been donated. If the bones are not suitable for any teaching purpose then they will be incinerated. It was through this process that a child skeleton turned up. On examination, it is probably also of Indian origin and the child would have been around 11 years old. It is clearly over a 100 years ago since it was made.

Placentas in pails

Another common item that is received as a donation is placentas. This is because individuals can take them home (or keep them at home) at the time of the birth and at some point, they can become forgotten. In one case a construction company was making changes to a building and found at the back of an understairs cupboard a placenta in a sealed bucket. The placenta was in good condition as it had been preserved in what I believed to be alcohol. Another example was a placenta found at the back of a cupboard by an individual who thought it must be her own placenta from her mum when she was a child. In both cases I chose not to keep the placenta. The laboratory has other examples that we use in teaching and so they were correctly disposed of.

Livers in lofts

There is also the example of where a retired Professor in anatomy had cleared through their loft and had some bones and a liver that had been impregnated with wax. These are beautiful specimens and have been added to our collection.

Some donations make me sad

On another occasion one of the team (Lucinda) had taken a call from a school who had a model they were no longer using. Lucinda said of course BSMS would take it and use it. They described it as a model of a baby. The school arranged delivery to us and then Lucinda started to get it out of the box. As she did she realised it was not quite as described and tried to run after the delivery person (who was from the school) but they had already gone. Lucinda phoned me to pop downstairs (my office is one level above the DR). On looking at the specimen it was clearly not a model at all but likely to be an actual fetus in a jar that was partially covered with fluid. The only way to find out for sure was to open the jar, but not knowing what chemicals the jar contained I had to consider our own health and safety. I directed Lucinda to put on our breathing masks and full personal protection equipment and, very carefully, I put my hands in the jar and lifted out the suspected fetus onto my palm. I now had no doubt, it was real. I could see the soft downy hair covering it. I could tell it was a girl and guessed the age to be around 20 weeks gestation (during pregnancy).

The fetus had no signs of disease or damage and despite being only partially covered by fluid it was clear they had been submerged for a long time in a substance such as formaldehyde. After returning the specimen to the jar the next thing I did was to contact the school and to try to establish some more facts about it. They were not very helpful and were not willing to speak to me. I had no other option but to raise it with the HTA, who helpfully contacted the school and pressed the importance of co-operating. The story behind this is that the fetus had been in the school for many, many years. I suspect they did know it was real or had a strong suspicion it might be. If they knew it was a model they would have thrown it away, rather than donating it to a medical school. However, there was no evidence that would point to this specimen coming from any illegal source. It is likely that sadly this specimen was the result of a miscarriage and by some means many years ago had ended up in a jar in a school.

Content that this was a historical specimen I was faced with the decision as to what to do next - keep it or dispose of it. Because it was in a good condition, I decided it could and would be used in teaching. It showed key anatomical/embryological points that would be useful in teaching this area. It could not be kept though in the jar it came in, so I tasked the technician with the job of re-potting it and creating a useable museum specimen out of it. They did the specimen justice by creating a new glass pot for it and carefully attaching it to a sheet of glass with very small clear ties so that it now looks like it is laying on its side in very clear fluid. Many features that can now be seen on this 20-week-old fetus are important for doctors in understanding the anatomy as applied to ultrasound scanning during pregnancy.

This is sadly not the only infant donation that I have received. An individual donated some bones. It was in lovely old box, carefully wrapped in paper. There were not just bones but also a child's head preserved in resin. The specimen itself was about the size of an eight-year-olds head. It has been dissected to show the protective structures that surround the brain. One eye has been dissected to show the muscles around the eye. The muscles surrounding the mouth had been dissected away and the facial artery had been injected with dye to highlight it. The use of resin is an old technique and I suspected that this specimen is a couple of hundred years old. On further investigation, with support from experts around the United Kingdom and support of colleagues in Clinical Imaging we undertook a Computed Tomography (CT) scan of the head, this confirm the head to be real and probably created in the Victorian era. Myself and colleagues are still working on this donation to gain information from carbon dating and from the teeth to identify when in history this specimen was made, where in the world it came from and more about it such as the diet of its 'owner'. We currently know nothing about how this child's head came to be where it is today.

Chapter 7. Global perspectives on body donation

The study of anatomy is very similar across the globe. The material to be studied isn't different (on the whole) but there are frequently local differences based on culture and processes. For example, countries that are predominantly Muslim have difficulty in obtaining donor bodies due to belief that the body must be buried within 24 hours. I have heard from international colleagues that in some cases to work around this they import donor bodies from a neighbouring country, but that this is not without its own problems. One fellow anatomist told me of how he dissected a donor to find the organs removed and the body stuffed full of drugs! They of course informed the police.

I have been fortunate to see anatomy in several different countries, and here are a couple of examples where a part of the process was very different from that of the United Kingdom.

United States of America

When donor supply is restricted, an option we have used is to import via companies in the United States as described previously, although these are expensive for teaching students.

The United States of America has over a hundred donation programs. It is also home to several companies who deal with body donation. The companies operate under a loophole in the legal system whereby they do not pay for donor bodies, but they are able to charge educators for the service to precure, store and distribute bodies or body parts. One company has been quoted in the media as making $27 million in the body parts trade. The media also quote that a typical brain bought in America will cost $750. There is worldwide debate and concern over the 'cadaveric commerce' these companies are generating. Due to local state laws there are just a few states where these companies cannot operate (New Jersey, Minnesota and Arkansas).

The companies takes the donor details at the time of death and undertakes a screening process from the information they are given to accept or reject the donation. Potential donors in twenty-one states can join these companies' registers before death, giving what equates in the United Kingdom as first person consent (AZ, CA, CT, DE, CO, FL, GA, IL, IN, MI, MO, NC, NV, NY, OH, OR, PA, TX, VA, WA & WI).

A part of the process that I do find concerning is that the information about that fact that donors could potentially be distributed to other countries is difficult to find, so a donor may donate not being clear that their body could be in several parts and flown to various countries and then be incinerated in three or four different continents.

It is also possible for someone else to donate another person's body (second person consent). This can include the bodies of those who die while under the care of the state. An article in Anatomical Sciences Education Journal 2011, titled 'My Body Belongs to Me (Not my family)' debates this and gives the example of a prisoner who died and was donated via second person consent to a medical school. As I see it, the question of ethics can be brought up as follows.

- Did his next of kin donate his body following his instruction?
- Did his next of kin decide that they did not want to organise a funeral?
- Did the next of kin donate his body as some sort of penance?
- Was there a next of kin?
- If not, is this a standard protocol by the prison to save on funeral expenses?

This is a very interesting ethical debate.

Many States and Medical Schools in the United States, including Florida and South Alabama Universities, run a donation program similar to the United Kingdom system. They do not offer any payment for the donation and use the donor within the state for the education of doctors and allied healthcare professionals. They do however, tend to permit second person consent donations. There has been concern raised from such schools that they now have a shortage of donors because individuals are donating to the large companies. This may be because of the advertising power of that these larger companies have at their disposal.

Some research institutions in America use donor bodies for other purposes. They include trauma research, for example how the skull reacts when subjected to different forces such as those sustained in a traffic accident or when riding a bike using or not using a helmet. In the United States, there are also 'Body Farms' that take donors to undertake specific experiments to understand aspects of how the body will decompose when left in certain conditions. As an example, a donated donor is left out in the woods for a week to determine the types of flies that would be attracted. These experiments help to ascertain the facts surrounding criminal cases. Currently, there are no Body Farms in the United Kingdom, although it has been reported in the media that the government is considering this.

Egypt

One of my first experiences of working with the Royal College of Surgeons overseas was in Cairo, Egypt, as an examiner testing junior surgeons' knowledge and skills. I was nervous and yet excited about what lay ahead. In Cairo, a bus collected us at 7.20 a.m. to take the examiners to the hospital. This was at a time when Cairo was in turmoil and protests had been violent. Our insurer had clearly stated to stay away from the main square. That morning though the bus, with an armed guard on it, drove straight through the main square. The hospital itself was military and I was soon settled into my examination station with a fellow examiner. It was a lovely old building with glass display cabinets full of unique historical medical items. The hosts brought over the anatomical specimens and my fellow examiner warned me I might not be used to them and he was right. They were expertly dissected, however the storage solution was very strong and made my eyes stream so much I could not work with them, so I used bones and models as props instead.

I arranged my props; a couple of ribs, vertebrae, scapula and model of a heart and was informed that I would also have a *'surface anatomy model'* (surface anatomy is the anatomy as it is viewed through the skin, so a model is just someone undressed). I thought great, we can do some surface landmarks of the lungs or regions supplied by nerves that are commonly affected in conditions. It wasn't to be. My surface model was a 17-year-old soldier (with a rifle) on attachment. As I was female he was forbidden to remove any clothing other than expose his ankle and forearm. Notwithstanding these obvious restrictions I brought in clinically relevant anatomy where I could. The language between us was very limited and I think he was nervous talking to me, but none the less always politely smiled. At breaks he was told he could sit down by his sergeant and I offered him a few sweets. During the examining my heart did race a few times as gunfire was heard outside, but the examiners were informed it was okay and so continued with the exams.

India

Again, I was due to examine junior surgeons overseas. At the University in Pune the hosts pleased to be hosting us for their surgical examinations (Figure 27). They were lovely people and very proud of the fact they had given us their best resources. In anatomy, this meant a room with a tiled floor, painted walls, a blackboard, and a table for us to sit at next to an open window with bars on it. Two fans in the ceiling whirred around but the thing you could not escape was the corpse on a stretcher covered with what was once a colourful Indian cloth (Figure 28) There are no regulations re photography and I have ensured in this figure that there are no identifiable features shown. The corpse had been fixed in formaldehyde and had been partly dissected. It looked awful and the smell of chemicals was very strong. There were powdered latex gloves put out for us to use, although these were not used by the technician who uncovered and got out some other prosections with his bare hands! I had not seen such gloves in many years. Previously I have had an allergic reaction to powdered gloves so I asked for some latex free gloves. They came back with a pair of sterile surgical gloves. I was really pleased as they were non-powdered, thicker and stronger than the disposal gloves. I worked on the corpse as best as I could and asked the examinees to locate certain anatomical structures. At lunchtime, I could not eat despite their hospitality. I think it was use of the bare hands to handle the cadaver that put me off. The candidates did very well and there was a fine ceremony afterwards. On the picture, my anatomy room is the window just to the right of the main door. A beautiful building (Figure 27).

As a group of examiners we then travelled to Hyderabad and delivered similar examination questions. This time I had been provided a not so well preserved body. Again, I carried on and opened it as best I could to show the examinees the structures I had to test them on. I had a great conversation with the very helpful technician. He was very surprised I did not procure my own bodies in the United Kingdom, or that I did not have a technician to procure bodies for me. It is considered acceptable for them to collect any dead body that they might see when out walking. The body they had brought me had been picked up off the streets 48 hours ago, embalmed and opened for me. Despite the use of unclaimed bodies being allowed in India there are still reports of there not being enough cadavers to meet demand. There are donation programmes in India but I have been informed that very few members of the public are aware of them.

I cannot imagine part of my role being to 'procure' bodies. I know historically it was the case, as with Robert Knox in Edinburgh. I don't think I could quite manage to pick up a dead body en-route to taking the kids to swimming!

Figure 27. University Medical School building

Figure 28. Inside the anatomy room (cadaver on stretcher on table).

Other countries

Other places where the practise varies from ours includes Africa, where most cadavers are unclaimed bodies from prisons and hospitals. Nigeria has additionally also reported the use of bodies of those who were bandits. Interestingly, because the medical schools in Africa were created when legislation was already established in other countries, there is no history of grave robbing. Turkey also uses unclaimed bodies and these make up around 80% of the cadavers used in the country. The remaining are from donation programs or are imported. Five medical schools in Turkey (out of 23) in 2018 had never taken a donated cadaver. The use of the unclaimed dead has led to the term *pauper cadaver*. It was also reported that in Africa there was a much higher proportion of male over female cadavers giving concern over the quality of teaching of the female reproductive system. A possible reason given for this was that females by their culture tended to stay closer to families who would ensure burial.

All of the literature detailing different types of donation programs in different countries are all united in the calling for an increase in the information made available to the public so that body donation can be made as a positive choice.

Chapter 8. Alternatives to using human donors and the future of donations

There are several alternatives to using human donation including models, 3D printing, imaging such as CT, Magnetic Resonance Imaging (MRI) and ultrasound. However, none of these do offer the experience of texture that human donation does.

Animal tissue

Of all of the above alternatives, none can offer the close experience of using human cadaveric material that use of animal tissue can. This can be a slightly difficult and sensitive issue. Back in history animals were regularly used for medical education. They were used to understand the human form, and to practice medical techniques. This is a slightly traditional approach but it still may have a place in medical education today. When I started my anatomy training at the University of Bristol students including myself trained on a range of animals. The undergraduate degree prepared students for a range of careers in veterinary, medicine, equine and science disciplines. It was therefore necessary that we studied the anatomy and function of animals and humans.

The animals included cats, dogs, sheep, cows and horses. The animals that were used for veterinary dissection had arrived either from a farm or from an abattoir. Veterinary dissection was undertaken at the Veterinary School in a large open DR. The lecturers carefully showed us how to use dissection instruments and how to employ our manual dexterity to carefully navigate the structure of these animals. A great deal of time was spent understanding how species differ and how the structure and function of the animal body is applied to modern veterinary and medical practice. It was only after undertaking these dissections that students could work on a human donor, as by then we had honed our skills on a more readily available resource.

At the time, students questioned little about the ethics of this practice. There was an awareness of the dangers of being associated with using animals and we were regularly reminded about animal activists. The university had previously suffered damage caused by a group of activists and one of our lecturers had received bomb threats. Practices that involve animals have greatly improved over the years. I really need to stress that I only work now with animal products that are destined for food or pet food production. In addition, I carefully consider the work that uses animals and if there is an alternative method.

Horse dissection

This is the exception to the food production line, the horses were donated to the Vet School by a local farm having been put down due to ill health. I was learning about the gastrointestinal system and our work one afternoon was to isolate, identify and study the different components of the equine gastrointestinal system. It was a very large job and a team of six of us wearing white coats and wellington boots started to identify the position of the stomach. The intestinal system had been removed from the horse and was now laid out on three metal tables in front of us. As I examined the stomach and noted the different layers of muscles, on cutting into the stomach, I examined the folds that increase the surface area and I could see what the horse had been eating.

Next I moved on to the small intestine, that seemed to go on for miles. The intricate blood and nerve supply was then dissected. I then came to a structure that is very different in humans, the cecum. The cecum is different because of its function - the cecum helps to process grass. A horse's cecum is a large muscular sac at the junction of the small and large intestine. It can hold 35 litres of water and matter, and it functions to help ferment material such as grass that has been ingested. In humans, the cecum is also at the junction of the small and large intestine but it is just a small blind ended sac that holds faecal matter. I really gained an understanding of the gastrointestinal system and had developed my dissection skills in an area of the body that is often wet and slippery. When it came to dissecting human gastrointestinal systems, I felt ready and could understand the structures I was looking for. If I had not had this valuable animal experience I would've certainly wasted a valuable human donor.

Pig Brain

I had been working on learning the complicated nerve tracts that head up and down the spinal cord that controlled many functions. I had been learning about where in the brain these nerve tracts ended. In groups of three we were given a brain and our task that afternoon was to dissect the brain and locate a series of structures. Again, in our white coats and wellies we made a start guided by a handbook. I had to cut the brain in half and then half again. I had to understand the difference between white and grey matter. The white matter is the nerve pathways and the grey matter the cell bodies of the nerve cells. I was also looking for nuclei that act as relay stations or end points for the nerve tracks. I especially enjoyed dissecting the cerebellum or *'little brain'* that is located at the base of your brain, because it is quite wrinkled and contains a great structure called the flocculonodular lobe. I left this session being really amazed all our thoughts and brain activity occurs in something that resembles the consistency of trifle!

Sheep Joints

I had been learning about the intricate structures of joints, especially the knee joint. I had gained a reasonable understanding of the basic structures from a book and from lectures. Once again, I am in the dissection laboratory in white coat and wellies. The sheep's legs had been removed and we had one leg between two of us on a table. Our instruction booklet told us how to remove the skin and examine the muscles that would be above the knee joint on the thigh. I examined the glistening white cartilage that made up the joint. It was very smooth and you could easily appreciate how the knee joint acts as a hinge and the surfaces glide over them. It was also easy to see how this cartilage in animals and humans could become torn or worn and that this would impede the mechanism. I took home from this practical a good idea of the spatial relations that I had gained during the dissection and an idea of the space within the joint. It felt quite avascular (without a blood supply) yet a very living part. The human knee joint does of course have some differences but when I first went into a human knee I was already trained to expect the toughness of the cartilage and had gained the spatial ability to know where to expect some of the supporting ligaments of the knee.

Simulation

All this experience as an undergraduate student helped prepare me for the work using animal tissue today. In some cases, the need to repeat or test new procedures is better undertaken on animals acquired from abattoirs. They offer very fresh tissue and the aim is to simulate human tissue. In these cases, it doesn't matter that the wider anatomy is slightly different, what matters here is the texture, the feel and the ability to undertake a procedure again and again. The University takes animal parts such as tracheas (wind pipes) or hearts that would not go into the human food chain and would be used to make pet food.

When animal material is used in the DR the team are extremely careful that it is separate from any human material. The tracheas would have been placed on metal trays and students would have worn disposable gowns, gloves and eye protection.

Simulation using animal tissue offers a high-quality experience for students and doctors to practice various clinical procedures. An example of medical students using animal material in simulation is in training of how to maintain an airway. Eight sheep tracheas (wind pipes) were used as part of a special study module for second year medical students. The students had been studying the anatomy of the neck and this optional module went into more depth on airway management. The students on this module first examined in detail the anatomy of the human trachea in the DR, then practiced on simulation dummies how to intubate, i.e. how to put a tube into the airway so that breathing can be forced to occur. The students then went into A&E to see this happening. The students came back to the DR with all this knowledge and experience and undertook various procedures on the sheep tracheas. These procedures included a tracheotomy, an emergency procedure that creates an entrance to the airway by going through the neck. To do this the students would have had to palpate (feel) the right membranous part of the trachea, first on themselves as living, then on a donor, and have noted the surrounding landmarks. They then would have come over to the sheep tracheas and palpate again before making an incision (cut) through the correct membrane. They then had to put in place the emergency breathing tube and secure it using stitches.

Some surgical courses for consultants do use a larger whole animal approach. For example, in trauma simulations cases surgeons can be set up with a pig or sheep torso that is placed and opened like it would be in the field simulating a battle injury. Army surgeons are trained in examples such as what to do if an explosive affects a soldiers leg. In this example, the surgeons work to isolate a large bleeding vessel through which fake blood can be pumped. They then practice how to amputate the leg quickly to reduce bleeding but also in a way that will reduce the future impact of the injury.

Animals in teaching and public engagement

Animal material is also used to teach a wide range of individuals. For example, the *Widening Access to Medicine'* sessions, where school students aged 15 to 18 are thinking about a career in medicine but come from areas, family backgrounds or schools where such aspirations would not be familiar. These students have opportunities to find out more about medicine, more about university and the life of being a medical student. Lessons for this group of students are in line with the level they would be learning at school but with a clinical scenario. Such sessions often include anatomy but these students are not permitted into the DR. Instead these students are taught using models and surface anatomy and they often get to use ultrasound just like our medical students do.

As already discussed, the opportunity to see and dissect at medical school is important and Widening Access to Medicine students can do just that but on animal parts. I often order intestines or hearts for this purpose. Using a different room away from the DR, these parts can be placed in trays and these students firstly get to learn how to wear protective material and how to handle a scalpel and other instruments. They then get to handle and examine the parts. In the case of the intestine they are guided to locate the different parts the stomach, small intestine (duodenum, jejunum, ileum) and the large intestine, keeping a good look out for the cecum and the appendix that is always present in animals. Once students have undertaken this and have linked the anatomical structure to how organs function I will talk about conditions that they might have heard about such as gastric ulcers, Crohn's disease and ulcerative colitis. The students then are guided to cut into the intestine and examine the internal structure, understanding where and how certain types of food is absorbed. They go on to find an artery or vein and can dissect it out to see it in greater detail. It is true that at school some simple dissection occurs for example, a sheep's heart, but sadly many schools do not do this. It is an excellent and cost effective way to bring the human body to life and for pupils to appreciate where and how diseases occur and the measures individuals can take to help prevent illness.

Operation Ouch
I was fortunate to be asked to be the expert anatomist for CBBC's Operation Ouch, a medical related education show for children produced by Maverick TV. I have assisted on five series and produced many of their animal dissections that you might have seen (Figure 29). I have enjoyed doing these based on the idea that hopefully a child and parent/guardian will be watching, having a cup of tea and learning what real lungs look like when they are inflated or what your ear drum might look like. Some of the dissections are easy, for example, demonstrating the intestines laid end to end (Figure 30). To do this I simply needed to cut along the edge of the colon and remove the connective tissue structure called a mesentery that holds all the arteries and veins that

supply the intestines. Once I was up and running with my scissors, despite a bit of mess, this probably took only 15 minutes.

Other dissections have proved a lot harder. It was very difficult to remove a pig's eardrum. It meant drilling through bone in the skull, you can see Catherine trying to get to it in the picture below (Figure 31). My favourite was the pig's anus (Figure 32). Again, this is material that is processed by the abattoir and was destined for the pet food trade. I asked the abattoir for the large intestine to anus complete with skin and they did not let me down. I spent a good 30 minutes carefully removing the correct amount of skin so that it was possible to see it was the end of the anus. It was difficult to dissect deep enough but not too deep down to show the anal sphincter. As you can imagine this sphincter is a bit of an unsung hero of the body, but we all know about it if it doesn't work! The anus dissection was used in filming. However, a week or so later I got a phone call from the TV company to say that the episode filming had become corrupted and could I re-dissect it. I said sure and within a couple of days a new anus arrived at the DR door. The producer waited while I repeated the procedure. They were then able to take away the second anus to complete the filming. It is nice to know that my dissections have had a TV viewing audience of over five million and if that improves someone's own health by developing their understanding of their own body, then I feel the aim has been achieved.

Figure 29. Filming for Operation Ouch with Dr. Chris & Dr. Xand

Figure 30. A Pigs intestines laid out.

Figure 31. Catherine removing the ear drum.

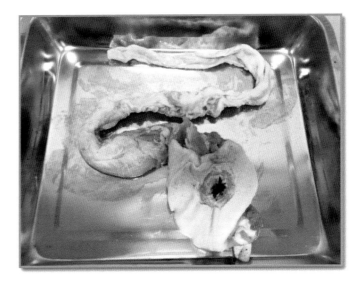

Figure 32. Animal anus dissection (the ring of muscle you can see around the anus is called puborectalis and helps with continence).

E-learning

The digital revolution has brought about some amazing resources to help students learn anatomy. These resources are often in the form of apps that can show a virtual body and from here you can virtually dissect, removing layers, clicking on structures to find out what they are, and rotating the image to see structures from a different perspective. Such apps are great but the current experience is still through a clean screen with no haptic (sensation through the fingertips) feedback. Other companies have produced apps that create a hologram of an anatomical structure in front of you. This is very 'cool' to see but still lacks the real experience. Students tell us time and time again that they like in-house produced material, that is made specific to their course. Strangely, students like to hear our voices and know that we have provided resources that reflect their course and examinations. Anatomists have produced e-learning material, instructional workbooks, online quizzes, podcasts and videos to help support students. Many of mine are on YouTube so that other students can use these too.

Virtual reality is also available for anatomy. You can follow the arteries going to the brain or can follow the flow of blood into the heart as if you are a red blood cell. These are very exciting advances. As technology increases these will get closer to reality. Again, what they currently lack is still the haptic feedback that you gain through your fingertips when you explore a real body part.

3D printing

One of the major advances in technology recently has been in 3D printing. For those who are novice to the concept, think of it like piping icing onto a cake, with the printer pressing out plastic that is built up in layers. On learning that 3D printers were becoming more common place four years ago, I had an idea that if I could print anatomical structures or organs then I could give these to students, very much like the old system of giving a student a skeleton. I felt it would help with their 3D learning and give them something tactile that they could inspect from all angles. Again, thanks to supportive colleagues this was made possible. The most important thing was to have a donor with the correct consent and not too many medical issues to put them through the CT scanner. This part of the project took nearly a year to get into place and there were many false starts. The donor needed to be recently deceased and the funeral services needed to be able to move them into the scanner before 8 a.m., before any patients were around. Everything aligned one bright early morning and after 45 minutes in the scanner the full body CT scan at the highest resolution the scanner could produce. The reason for using a donor rather than a living person was that it meant the scanner could be used at the highest setting without risk of toxicity. After this the donor was taken to be embalmed and studied as we had planned.

The data set was amazing and it was soon possible to produce 3D prints; a spine, a heart, a foot, et cetera (Figure 33). Importantly, I wanted to understand how the use of 3D prints had impacted on students' learning so I conducted a study by dividing the year into two groups. One had access to 3D prints the other didn't. The groups were then swapped for a following module. The result was that using 3D prints in non-dissection sessions and for personal study increased students' knowledge of anatomy. This supported mine and others' research that shows that teachers need to ensure 3D training is part of medical education. I was the first in the United Kingdom to be making 3D prints for our students and I have shared our experiences of developing these resources to other teachers through seminars and workshops (Figure 34).

There are some companies who have made simulation models through 3D printing in softer plastics. However, it is still not like the real thing. The muscles are clearly attached by pins to bones and you can remove them to look underneath. In real people when you lift a muscle it is separated from the muscle underneath by fascia (a connective tissue like structure that binds everything in the body together). Currently in a simulation model you can see where the muscles are but you do not gain a true experience of how they connect to surround structures and what they look and feel like.

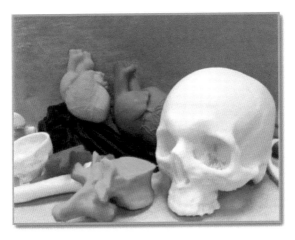

Figure 33. 3D prints (Skull, heart and vertebrae)

Figure 34. Dr. Smith training teachers on the importance of 3D learning.

I have continued to use 3D printing and now have a variety of prints from a wide range of sources, some from CT data and others from shared repositories. This is one very exciting area that I think will develop and might change the use of donors. It will be possible to one day print a whole donor. It is already possible to print cells onto a scaffold (support framework), so I think that it will be possible to print a dead body made up of cells. If this is achieved it might be end for anatomists using donors but I think this is way off yet.

Will donors always be needed?

As things currently stand donors are in need more than ever. The United Kingdom government in 2017 has permitted an increase of 25% in the number of medical student university places. Unlike other degrees the numbers in medicine are nationally capped and a university is fined if it goes over its agreed quota. This cap is there to ensure that the number of students in training as medical students matches the number of posts available at qualification and that the numbers going forward into sub-specialities, such as surgery, are also controlled. This rise in medical school places will increase the need for donors in universities that have donor programmes.

There are three United Kingdom medical schools that at time of writing do not use any form of donor material - Exeter, Plymouth and Lancaster. Instead they teach using other methods such as models, ultrasound and e-learning. There are also new Medical Schools starting that are choosing to establish donor programmes or link into existing donor programmes, such as the London Anatomy Office.

The way medical schools use donors is changing as more are starting to use a *'soft fix'* embalming that gives a more *'life like'* feel and ability of tissues to move and glide over each other. Dissection for the sake of dissection is no longer the case and medical schools carefully plan their curriculum and teaching sessions to ensure that the learning of anatomy is highly integrated into clinical practice. For example, students dissect or study a prosection of the heart while the following day they are learning about medicines that work on the heart or how a heart attack is treated.

Tied into this integrated learning is e-learning or technology enhanced learning. Today's generation of students are online 24/7 and the days of learning being limited to the 9-5 hours of the DR and library are gone. I have no plans to operate a 24/7 DR but I recognise the need for students to be able to continue their learning when they have left the DR.

I feel that medical schools should offer students a wide range of experiences and that an ideal anatomy curriculum would contain learning experiences with real human cadaver supported by other learning methods such as virtual reality. Through my own research and that of others, it is known that using donors increases anatomical understanding and many facets of spatial ability, such as judging depth, that are important in many clinical procedures. There are also many non-technical skills such as ethics, communication and team working that are fostered through learning experiences on donors.

Mobile anatomy unit

One possible future option for anatomy is to move to a more mobile provision, so that it can be delivered at hospital or conference venues where and when there is a training need. The number of courses that medical schools run for qualified doctors and health care professionals has increased in recent years. These are the courses that are run for surgeons, anaesthetists, obstetricians, gynaecologists, et cetera, who use predominantly soft fix or fresh frozen donor material to practice techniques or to refine new ones. It was this that led to a surgical company requesting a mobile anatomy unit in collaboration with BSMS.

In the United States, mobile units are used by specific surgical companies to take fresh frozen material to a hospital and to provide on the site training. This reduces the need for the clinician to travel and means that in-between operating lists they can visit and re-evaluate a procedure or explore a new approach.

A mobile anatomy fresh frozen unit had not been undertaken in the United Kingdom before. I had been working with the company involved for four years and understood their need to have such a unit at the world gathering of foot surgeons in Brighton. Most importantly I trusted the individuals I was working with. They knew this was a first for the United Kingdom, they knew if anything happened it would affect me professionally and the University of Sussex HTA licence. With lots of consultation with the HTA and the university legal team permission was granted to proceed.

The decision was made to use feet imported from the United States that would be received under my licence, stored, defrosted and then packed into a secure box and transported by myself and another member of my team to the mobile operating unit at the Brighton Centre (Figure 35). In advance all security issues had been considered and the feet were under the watchful eye of my team member always. Then at the end of the day the feet would be returned to our DR for overnight storage. The course ran like this for three days and it was exhausting for all involved. The result though was that over 80 surgeons who specialise in foot surgery from around the world had the opportunity to learn the new techniques that had been discussed in the conference. While the DR is only 30 minutes from the Brighton Centre, if this course had run back at the DR I suspect only 10, maybe 20 would have made that journey and the all-important context would have been delayed.

Figure 35. Mobile operating theatre for simulation (the open side door is showing the air handling facility).

Chapter 9. A Personal touch

I often get asked what it is like working with the dead. Depending on the time and place, if appropriate I politely joke *'they don't answer back!'* The real answer is that it can be quite strange. You do get used to it, however it does affect you. I try to just process it. Working with dead bodies has made me face up to my own mortality and at times has clearly affected me and my ability to undertake my role. Our minds process information in various ways and one of these ways is in dreams.

Anatomical dreams

I think everyone dreams of work at times, it is our minds way of processing information and for me and other anatomists this has been no different.

My dreams
There are a few dreams that I can very clearly remember. In one dream, I walked into the DR to see eight fresh frozen individuals that had come from overseas. The donors were deep frozen and the team were setting up the DR and turning the donors to ensure equal defrosting. It was then I noticed one eye on a donor was twitching. I did not pay any attention to it but when the prosector went to turn that donor they moved and curled up into the fetal position. It turned out that this donor had come back to life and was capable of moving. What next ensued was that the team ran frantically around, trying to call the police because no one knew what else to do with a reanimated corpse from another country, what would you do? It was then discovered that the donor's lover had sneaked in the shipping container and that he was also alive. In the end, despite a lot of panic, we let the happy couple go free to continue their life in the United Kingdom and everyone is then found in an old English pub!

In a previous dream, I was in the old concrete building at Southampton, where the corridors were rumoured to be haunted. I was in my office that used to be an old laboratory, with a teak wooden bench down one side and an old white porcelain sink. I became aware of 'donors' walking down the corridor, effectively holding me to ransom as I could not move or exit my office as they had a military style patrol going on outside.

In a different dream, I dreamt I had a pick-up truck and that I had a few prosections of legs in the back. For some reason, I had buried them in my garden. The dream part of this was very vivid. I had buried them just down from the apple tree in our old garden. I had no idea why in the dream I had done this. They had come from work, they could go back to work. Then a while later my boss at the time was in my garden and they noticed the area where the legs were and could see the plastic bags that are used just poking out of the soil. I tried to cover it up, saying it was just garden plastic. I then remember trying to dig them up months later and they were still in good condition and taking them back into work and that was it end of dream. I promise this has never happened in real life!

Colleagues' dreams

I know other anatomists have dreams about donors too. My good colleague Dr. Gabrielle Finn (Hull York Medical School, United Kingdom) explained that in one dream she had, not long after her mother passed away, she was uncovering a donor and started to dissect it when it turned out to be her mother.

Another colleague, Dr. Danielle Royer (University of Colorado, United States) explained her reoccurring dream, where she dreamt she was in bed. One of the donors, an elderly female, was lying naked in the bed. The donor's back was towards Danielle and the donor was curled up in the fetal position. Danielle could then see her hand holding a scalpel and would approach the back of the donor lying next to her and start to make a midline incision. This reflected the first cut she had made in the dissection session.

Dr. Mike Pascoe (University of Colorado, United States) explained how he dreams about performing dissection and that his dreams increase in frequency during the course where he was performing dissection. Other anatomists have explained how they have dreamed about attending the donor's funeral. One fellow anatomist once described a dream where they were eating at a restaurant and all they could focus on was that a nerve in their leg had fallen out of their skin and was hanging about, interrupting their ability to enjoy the meal.

Maybe this is our brain's way of processing and coping with the things that are seen. In every aspect of our life it is important to have a support system that means you can rationalise and make peace with issues. One support system that my colleagues and I initiated at Southampton was to sit on the beanbag in the office and eat a banana if one of us was upset. This signalled to others that support was needed without having to say it or having the boss know. Anyone who works in an environment that is considered stressful or where difficult issues arise, knows that they need to look after their own mental health. I don't think anyone who works with death or other difficult circumstances can go through their professional life and not be affected. It would make us unhuman. Everyone has their own ways of normalising what we see and do. I think humour (appropriately placed) can help, as can having supportive colleagues and family.

Death and dying

It would be strange not to include anything in this book about dying. Death and dying is still very much a taboo subject in society but to get to death you must die. To see and understand the process of dying has really helped me work with the dead.

My first death

My first experience of seeing someone die was in a hospital when I was working as a Health Care Assistant (HCA). I would have been 17 or 18 years old and this was at Bournemouth hospital. I was working on Ward 4 nicknamed *'Ward 4 Death's Door'*. At the time, I had not worked on this ward before but the team were welcoming at shift changeover. The ward specialised in elderly care. At the shift change (handover) it was explained that the gentleman in the side room was dying but had no family. The doctors had checked on him and I was assigned the job of sitting with him and keeping an eye on things. I had had no training for this at all. Going in I could see he was a frail old gentleman lying in a hospital gown moving his arms around every now and again. He was incontinent so my first job was to clean him up. He then became a bit more still and over the next hour or so his breathing pattern changed as if he was snatching for breath. I had to pop in and out of his room and had checked with the nurse that all the care he needed, medication, et cetera, had been given. She said they were just waiting for the inevitable and that as it got close I should check on him more. So, I did. I tried to talk to him. I didn't know what to say but said things that I felt would be appropriate. I think they were things like *'relax, your loved ones would be thinking of you'*. I don't know if he could hear me but they say that hearing is the last sense to go. I also don't know if it was appropriate but I wanted him to know he was not alone so I held his hand. It felt the right thing to do. I know he knew someone was there as he squeezed my hand a little. Not long after he took his last breath and then quite quickly colour drained from him.

I went out to get the nurse who came back in, shut his eyes and opened the window. She said opening the window allowed the soul to leave him. The nurse and I then washed him and got him ready for the porters to come and collect him. There weren't any relatives to phone. I was then allowed to go on my break and I remember walking the long walk to the canteen trying to compute what I had experienced. I wasn't shocked, it was just new.

Further deaths that I have experienced in a clinical environment were easier to process but still upsetting. I was surprised at the experience of undertaking chest compressions in an operating theatre where the patient became unstable very quickly and went into cardiac arrest. Despite all the efforts of the team, she died. It made me really think about how quick death can be.

In some ways though this experience did help prepare me for watching my own grandparents and father die.

Impact of personal deaths of loved ones

The impact of this on my professional life each time has been different. In the case of my Grandmother, she had fallen over in her nursing home. She was already suffering with Alzheimer's and in the fall had fractured her femur (thigh bone), which they had to operate on otherwise she would have died. The operation went well but the anaesthetic was problematic and I went up to recovery to see her. I knew it was close and she was ready to go. I just sat there and held her hand. I knew she was tough (Mum and Dad were travelling back from being overseas) and she pulled through and after a few weeks she went back to her nursing home. It was not long after that she passed away, her body and mind finally worn out. After her death and her funeral, the work was difficult, every female donor's face reminded me of her.

I found my Grandpa's death harder to face when back at work. He had been in Bournemouth hospital and was very ill. The nurse explained it was likely to be hours. Again, Mum and Dad were overseas and were heading home (this sounds like they were always away, they weren't it was just bad luck!). I didn't think they would make it, but I knew Grandpa would do everything he could to see his only son (my Dad) and he held on. I was called one morning when working at Southampton Hospital by Bournemouth Hospital saying it was getting close. I drove as fast as my car would go down the M27 and A35. When I arrived, he was towards the end. He was in a side room, not on Ward 4 but the ward next door. He was grey and his breathing pattern was snatched. I sat next to him and held his hand and talked to him. Talking to him was easy, he was a greengrocer by trade, he liked the simple things in life, watching the sea, growing a bit of veg in his garden. He had always been kind and easy going so I just talked to him. Mum and Dad made it. I knew he could hear Dad and it was as if things were complete and he could finally let go and hours later his breath became more and more shallow and infrequent and he passed away.

Back at work a few days later, I could not face going into the DR without crying, but I knew I had to pull myself together. I had a head and neck session to teach with my good colleague Dr. Scott Border. The session started with a short introduction that would use the video camera so students could see smaller structures on a bigger screen. My job while Scott was speaking was to move the camera and then teach the rest of the practical. The period between this practical and my Grandad's death was too short and I ended up crying in front of the students. Scott was very supportive and I explained that it was too early to see heads, especially male ones, with mouths open that reminded me of my Granddad. I was still processing the grief. I left the practical and didn't teach for a few weeks.

I have always wondered if being surrounded by the dead has made it easier when family or friends deaths have occurred. I am under no illusion as to what a dead body looks like and that death is final for the physical form. I think my work has helped a bit. My Dad's death was slightly different as he had only nine days between a terminal diagnosis that his skin cancer had spread and death. The doctors told him it would be four to six months. Those nine days went by in a flash and Mum and I were with him at the end. I will never forget those last breaths in the hour before, the colour draining very quickly out of him and his hand becoming cold very quickly. He was only 66 and I miss him every day. When I returned to work it was June and it was time for the annual placing of donors in their coffins. I went into the DR but again couldn't bear to be reminded of death. I knew I could not do two things. I could not go through the process of the coffins, having just buried one I loved, and I also knew that having spoken at Dad's funeral I could not attend the service of memorial for our donors.

I am fortunate to have a supportive deputy, Dr. Andrew Dilley who, together with the team, undertook both these duties for me. I did, however, feel it was important to explain my actions to the students and sent out an e-mail saying my emotions were just too raw. I was really taken aback by the kind and understanding replies I had. I hope it reflected that I had always tried to understand when students had experienced issues with being in the DR and that I was now in that circumstance. It didn't feel great for me though, a Head of Anatomy, who couldn't go into their own anatomy laboratory. I gave it a few weeks and then decided Dad would not have wanted anything of his death to have affected me in a negative way and I went back into the DR. It was now summer and the DR was full of surgical courses and it felt better. When term started again in September, I was back to normal. It is with every new donor that comes in and with every donor whom I return to their families that I reminded of their death and of those who are close to me. Being surrounded by death does make me appreciate the gift of life.

Chapter 10. About the Author and this book

How did I get into anatomy?

Well I can't say I fell into this career by accident; neither can I say I woke up one day and thought that is what I want to do. Neither can I say that it was part of careers advice at school (imagine that), or that I was so inspired by an anatomist (only a few might have heard of the likes of Versalis), or that it was because of that famous anatomy TV programme *'Gray's Anatomy'.* As an aside, I must confess it winds me up that whenever I want to Google something academic with the word anatomy or Henry Gray in it, the results go straight to this TV show. However, I know many love the programme and I don't mind that.

My pathway into this career was anything but plain sailing. I wasn't very bright at school. I wasn't even going to be allowed to sit my GCSEs (Age 16 school examinations). This was because of having to deal with a mixture my own health problems (epilepsy) and just not getting on at school. I started to take an interest in how the body worked through my hobby of dancing. I was also interested in my own medical condition. This is before the internet and I would look up the nervous system in the library or book shops. I slowly started to get on at school and eventually did take my GCSEs and went on to take my A-Levels (Age 18 school examinations).

Following my interest in the human body I undertook my first degree in Anatomy (Animal and Human) at the University of Bristol and then qualified as a teacher at the University of Surrey. I commenced my career at the University of London, St George's Hospital Medical School working as an anatomy demonstrator. I had undertaken a teaching placement at St George's and when this ended I was asked to continue working with them. My roles included teaching of medical and allied health care students. I was also involved in the preparation of donated bodies for teaching. This role involved carefully removing the skin to show the muscles underneath. This experience helped improve my dissection and teaching skills.

I then took up a post as Teaching Fellow at the University of Southampton, remaining at Southampton Medical School for twelve years. During six of those I completed a part time PhD in Anatomy Education and worked my way up through the academic ladder to Lecturer and then Senior Lecturer. I then moved along the coast to take up my current role as a Reader and Head of Anatomy at the Brighton and Sussex Medical School, University of Sussex.

How this book came about

I needed peace to write this and almost permission from myself, this is not a widely-shared profession. Anatomy has a notorious history, with the likes of Burke and Hare, but it is very different in the 21st century even if most of the anatomy has not changed. Permission to write this arrived in 2015. It was the Anatomical Society Winter meeting at Cambridge, a usual meeting. The Anatomical Society has two conferences a year when Anatomists from around the UK, Ireland and other countries gather. When I started attending in 2002 it was quite stuffy and full of middle aged white men but thanks to Professor Susan Standring and the society members it has been turned around and is a vibrant and essential supportive network for anatomists.

At the conference you present a recent piece of research, either through a poster or a presentation. At this conference, I had a poster based on a piece of educational research to present. The poster sessions are always a highlight of the conference. It is much more relaxed in that you stand by your poster that contains new and exciting research and members of the society come and ask you questions. I enjoy these sessions as the friendly questions often make you think wider or you end up joining up with colleagues for future projects.

Conferences are a chance to speak to lots of colleagues, catch up and network with new people. They are also important for the general conversations about a profession and anatomy is no different. Yes, anatomists do sit around and discuss body parts! Anatomists often talk and support each other over the trials and tribulations of academic life. They also talk about anatomy research. Many things have been discovered over the years and are still being found. Only last year a new ligament in the knee was found and the well-known '*quadriceps*' group of muscles in the thigh were found to be five and now should be maybe known as the '*quinticept*'!

Due to holding roles on the Anatomical Society Council (Figure 36), at this event I was informed where to sit at dinner, on the top table at Magdalene College. I had put my coat in at this very impressive college with a 600-year history and I headed up to the top table. Until this night at Cambridge I had not disclosed the idea of this book to anyone in the anatomy community. A few people knew, my husband and my friend Jo who I told when away camping. I was sitting next to a historian at the event in Cambridge who has was talking about the Anatomy Society's history and about autobiographies. I decided then to confess and say that I was writing this. What I got from this incredibly intense interaction was a sense of pride that what I had been working on was of interest and I was worthy of writing it and that I had a story to tell. Little by little I shared the idea of this book with colleagues and all were supportive.

So, another few years followed and this book just sat as a file on my MacBook, being added to as and when time allowed. I started to receive lots of Freedom of Information requests from journalists about body donation (about one a month) and I realised that the public were perhaps more interested in this option than I had realised. I do not have anything against a journalist publishing a piece on body donation but I felt it was time that there was a piece written from the inside. The time for this book had arrived, it was now time to put my head above the academic parapet and publish this. I feel there is a genuine interest in death and what people can do with their bodies. I feel it is also time to increase the transparency of this from a personal perspective. I hope you have found this interesting, perhaps even inspiring and I realise at times it might have been upsetting. I hope that it portrays real life and death. If I have opened your eyes or created a positive thought or action that is more than I could hope for.

Figure 36. Anatomical Society Council when the Society was awarded its Coat of Arms (2015). *(Front Row left to right Professor Stefan Przyborski, Dr. Claire Smith, Mr. William Hunt, Windsor Herald, Professor Clive Lee, Mr Keith Lawrey, Learned Societies Officer, Professor Abigail Tucker, Assistant Professor Siobhan Loughna. Back row left to right. Dr. David Heylings, Ms. Mary-Anne Piggott, Professor Zoltán Molnár, Professor Emeritus Colin Ockleford, Associate Professor Lopa Leach, Dr. Adam Taylor, Professor D. Ceri Davies, Professor Kieran McDermott, Professor Fabio Quondamatteo, Dr. Joy Balta, Dr. Grenham Ireland, Professor Simon H. Parson.)*

Final Word- To the Silent Teachers

I would like to acknowledge all those who contribute in their own unique way to the discipline of anatomy. Everyone who is named in this book has given their permission to be named, if you know me or work in the sector you can probably guess a few more.

I acknowledge this book is my experience and my perception. I hope for you, the reader, I have given you an insight into the discipline of anatomy. If you have been thinking of donating, I hope I have not put you off. Medicine would not be where it is today without anatomy donors, from the early dissections that discovered each organ to every day when a medical student sees and feels a structure. That knowledge and understanding they will use when they become a doctor. In the words of one of my students 'a lesson surpassing that of any scholar'.

If you are a relative or a friend of a donor I hope that you feel that your loved one's contribution has been worthwhile and that they have been treated with the dignity that I would afford to my own family.

A doctor treats over 40,000 patients in their working lifetime. A donor typically will be dissected and or examined as prosections by 20 to 200 medical students. In addition, the donor will help to train many already qualified doctors who are developing their knowledge and skills. Therefore, one single donation could affect the lives of around ten million patients.

To the Silent Teachers- with all my respect, admiration and gratitude.

Acknowledgements

Firstly, my eternal gratitude to each donor, their family and friends. Their gift is truly inspiring and has led to the improvement of millions of other people's lives.

This book would not have been possible without the support of Brighton and Sussex Medical School. To all my colleagues in the anatomy community you know who you are - you are an amazing and supportive group of people. I hope that I have accurately portrayed our work in this book. Special thanks to Kim at the London Anatomy Office for her help in the accuracy of information.

To my friends, who have put up with strange conversations during walks, camping trips, pubs and dinners. It really is your fault for asking! You are the ones who have made me realise my job is a privilege and that the public have the right to know more about body donation if they wish. Thank you. Special thanks to Kris and Jeff for their helpful comments on various drafts.

Lastly, thank you to my family who have always supported me, my mum Susan, my husband Trevor and my children Hermione and Elodie. In loving memory of my dad, Michael.

Crew List

Thank you to everyone listed below for their support and for agreeing to be named in the book.

Dr. Scott Border, Principle Teaching Fellow, University of Southampton.

Ms. Lydia Carline, Prosector, Brighton and Sussex Medical School.

Ms. Kim Claridge, Office Manager, London Anatomy Office.

Professor Ceri Davies, Imperial College London.

Dr. Andrew Dilley, Senior Lecturer, Brighton and Sussex Medical School.

Mr. Martin Drew, Funeral Director, Dignity Funerals.

Ms. Lucinda Evans, Anatomy Technician, Brighton and Sussex Medical School.

Dr. Gabrielle Finn, Senior Lecturer, Hull York Medical School.

Ms. Catherine Hennessey, Teaching Fellow, Brighton and Sussex Medical School.

Ms. Sarah Llewellyn, Donations Co-ordinator, London Anatomy Office.

Dr. Mike Pascoe, University of Colorado, United States.

Dr. Danielle Royer, University of Colorado, United States.

List of United Kingdom Medical Schools

Institution	Postcodes	Contact Number
Bristol University	BA, BS, EX, GL, PL, TA, TQ, TR	0117 928 7415
Cambridge University	AL, CB, CM, CO, HP, IP, LU, PE, SG	0122 333 3776
Cardiff University	CF, LD, NP, SA, SY (Welsh Counties)	0292 087 4370
Hull York Medical School	DN14-37, HU, YO	0148 246 4750
Keele University	CW, LL, SK 10-11-17, ST, TF, WS	0178 273 4690
Leeds University	BD, CA, HD, HG, HX, LS, WF	0113 343 4297
Leicester University	CV, LE, MK, NN	0116 252 3082
Liverpool University	BB, CH, FY, IM, L, LA, PR, WA, WN	0151 794 5442
London Anatomy Office	BN, BR, CR, CT, DA, E, EC, EN, GU, HA, IG, KT, ME, N, NW, RH, RM, SE, SL, SM, SS, SW, TN, TW, UB, W, WC, WD	0207 848 8042
Manchester University	BL, M, OL, SK (all but 10-11-17)	0161 275 5241
Newcastle University	NE, SR, TS	0191 208 6616
Norwich	NR	0160 359 1104
Nottingham University	DE, DH, DL, LN, NG	0115 823 0143
Oxford University	OX, RG, SN	0186 527 2181
Queen's Belfast University	BT	028 9097 2131

Scotland	AB, DD, DG, EH, FK, G, IV, KA, ML, PA, PH, TD, ZE	0131 244 2711
Sheffield University	DN1-13, S	0114 222 4642
Southampton University	BH, DT, PO, SO, SP	0238 120 5763

(Data from institutions' websites, accurate at time of publishing 2018)